INDEX TO TITLES

3

INDEX TO TITLES

4

PERCY BYSSHE SHELLEY

PERCY BYSSHE SHELLEY, English poet, was born at
Field Place, Essex, in 1792; drowned in the Bay of
Spezia, Italy, in 1822. He studied at Eton and
Oxford, and later went to make his home in Italy,
where all his best known poems were written. Although he wrote a number of long poems, his fame
rests on his short pieces and lyrics. Among his
best poems are: "Queen Mab," his first poem;
"The Revolt of Islam," "The Cenci," "Hellas," "To
a Skylark" and "Ode to the West Wind."

TRIBUTE TO AMERICA

(From "The Revolt of Islam")

THERE is a people mighty in its youth,
  A land beyond the oceans of the west,
Where, though with rudest rites, Freedom and
      Truth
Are worshipped. From a glorious mother's breast
Who, since high Athens fell, among the rest,
Sate like the Queen of Nations, but in woe,
By inbred monsters outraged and oppressed,
Turns to her chainless child for succor now,
It draws the milk of power in Wisdom's fullest
      flow.

That land is like an eagle, whose young gaze
Feeds on the noontide beam, whose golden plume
Floats moveless on the storm, and in the blaze
Of sunrise gleams when earth is wrapped in gloom;

An epitaph of glory for the tomb
Of murdered Europe may thy fame be made,
Great people! As the sands shalt thou become;
Thy growth is swift as morn when night must fade;
The multitudinous earth shall sleep beneath thy
      shade.

Yes, in the desert there is built a home
For Freedom. Genius is made strong to rear
The monuments of man beneath the dome
Of a new heaven; myriads assemble there
Whom the proud lords of man, in rage or fear,
Drive from their wasted homes. . . .
Nay, start not at the name, America! . . .

ODE TO THE WEST WIND

O WILD West Wind, thou breath of Autumn's
    being,
    Thou from whose unseen presence the leaves
    dead

Are driven like ghosts from an enchanter fleeing,
Yellow, and black, and pale, and hectic red,
Pestilence-stricken multitudes: O thou,
Who chariotest to their dark, wintry bed

The wingèd seeds, where they lie cold and low,
Each like a corpse within its grave, until
Thine azure sister of the Spring shall blow

Her clarion o'er the dreaming earth, and fill
(Driving sweet buds like flocks to feed in air)
With living hues and odors plain and hill:

Wild Spirit which art moving everywhere,
Destroyer and preserver: hear, oh, hear!

ODE TO THE WEST WIND

Thou on whose stream, 'mid the steep sky's commotion
Loose clouds like earth's decaying leaves are shed,
Shook from the tangled boughs of heaven and
   ocean,

Angels of rain and lightning: there are spread
On the blue surface of thine airy surge,
Like the bright hair uplifted from the head

Of some fierce Mænad, even from the dim verge
Of the horizon to the zenith's height,
The locks of the approaching storm. Thou dirge

Of the dying year, to which this closing night
Will be the dome of a vast sepulcher,
Vaulted with all thy congregated might

Of vapors, from whose solid atmosphere
Black rain, and fire, and hail, will burst: oh hear,

Thou who didst waken from his summer dreams
The blue Mediterranean where he lay,
Lulled by the coil of his crystalline streams

Beside a pumice isle in Baiæ's bay,
And saw in sleep old palaces and towers
Quivering within the wave's intenser day,

All overgrown with azure moss and flowers
So sweet, the sense faints picturing them! Thou
For whose path the Atlantic's level powers

Cleave themselves into chasms, while far below
The sea-blooms and the oozy weeds which wear
The sapless foliage of the ocean know

Thy voice, and suddenly grow gray with fear,
And tremble and despoil themselves: oh, hear!

If I were a dead leaf thau mightest bear;
If I were a swift cloud to fly with thee;
A wave to pant beneath thy power, and share

The impulse of thy strength, only less free
Than thou, O uncontrollable! if even
I were as in my boyhood, and could be

The comrade of thy wanderings over heaven,
As then, when to outstrip thy skyey speed
Scarce seemed a vision— I would ne'er have striven

As thus with thee in prayer in my sore need.
Oh, lift me as a wave, a leaf, a cloud!
I fall upon the thorns of life!   I bleed!

A heavy weight of hours has chained and bowed
One too like thee—tameless, and swift, and proud.

Make me thy lyre, even as the forest is:
What if my leaves are falling like its own!
The tumult of thy mighty harmonies

Will take from both a deep autumnal tone,
Sweet though in sadness. Be thou, Spirit fierce,
My spirit! Be thou me, impetuous one!

Drive my dead thoughts over the universe,
Like withered leaves, to quicken a new birth;
And, by the incantation of this verse,

Scatter, as from an unextinguished hearth
Ashes and sparks, my words among mankind!
Be through my lips to unawakened earth

The trumpet of a prophecy! Oh, Wind,
If Winter comes, can Spring be far behind?

TO A SKYLARK

HAIL to thee, blithe spirit!
   Bird thou never wert,
That from heaven, or near it,
   Pourest thy full heart
In profuse strains of unpremeditated art.

Higher still and higher
   From the earth thou springest
Like a cloud of fire;
   The blue deep thou wingest,
And singing still dost soar, and soaring ever singest.

In the the golden lightning
   Of the sunken sun,
O'er which clouds are bright'ning,
   Thou dost float and run,
Like an unbodied joy whose race is just begun.

The pale purple even
   Melts around thy flight;
Like a star of heaven,
   In the broad daylight
Thou art unseen, but yet I hear thy shrill delight,

Keen as are the arrows
   Of that silver sphere
Whose intense lamp narrows
   In the white dawn clear
Until we hardly see, we feel that it is there.

All the earth and air
   With thy voice is loud,
As, when night is bare,
   From one lonely cloud
The moon rains out her beams, and heaven is over-
     flowed.

9

What thou art we know not;
  What is most like thee?
From rainbow-clouds there flow not
  Drops so bright to see
As from thy presence showers a rain of melody.

Like a poet hidden
  In the light of thought,
Singing hymns unbidden,
  Till the world is wrought
To sympathy with hopes and fears it heeded not:

Like a high-born maiden
  In a palace tower,
Soothing her love-laden
  Soul in secret hour
With music sweet as love which overflows her
    bower:

Like a glow-worm golden
  In a dell of dew,
Scattering unbeholden
  Its aërial hue
Among the flowers and grass which screen it from
    the view:

Like a rose embowered
  In its own green leaves,
By warm winds deflowered,
  Till the scent it gives
Makes faint with two much sweet those heavy-
    winged thieves:

Sound of vernal showers
  On the twinkling grass;
Rain-awakened flowers—
  All that ever was
Joyous and clear and fresh—thy music doth sur-
    pass.

Teach us, sprite or bird,
   What sweetened thoughts are thine;
I have never heard
   Praise of love or wine
That panted forth a flood of rapture so divine.

Chorus hymeneal
   Or triumphal chaunt,
Matched with thine, would be all
   But an empty vaunt—
A thing wherein we feel there is some hidden want.

What objects are the fountains
   Of thy happy strain?
What fields, or waves, or mountains?
   What shapes of sky or plain?
What love of thine own kind? What ignorance of
     pain?

With thy clear, keen joyance
   Languor cannot be:
Shadow of annoyance
   Never came near thee:
Thou lovest, but ne'er knew love's sad satiety.

Waking or asleep,
   Thou of death must deem
Things more true and deep
   Than we mortals dream,
Or how could thy notes flow in such a crystal
     stream?

We look before and after,
   And pine for what is not:
Our sincerest laughter
   With some pain is fraught,
Our sweetest songs are those that tell of saddest
     thought.

Yet, if we could scorn
    Hate and pride and fear,
If we were things born
    Not to shed a tear,
I know not how thy joy we ever should come near.

Better than all measures
    Of delightful sound,
Better than all treasures
    That in books are found,
Thy skill to poet were, thou scorner of the ground!

Teach me half the gladness
    That thy brain must know,
Such harmonious madness
    From my lips would flow,
The world should listen then as I am listening now.

AN ELEGY ON THE DEATH OF JOHN KEATS

(Stanzas selected from " Adonais "

I

I WEEP for Adonais—he is dead.
    Oh, weep for Adonais, though our tears
Thaw not the frost which binds so dear a head;
    And thou, sad hour, selected from all years
    To mourn our loss, rouse thy obscure compeers,
And teach them thine own sorrow! Say, "With me
Died Adonais! Till the Future dares
Forget the Past, his fate and fame shall be
An echo and a light unto eternity."

IV

Most musical of mourners, weep again!
  Lament anew, Urana! He died,
Who was the sire of an immortal strain,
  Blind, old, and lonely, when his country's pride,
  The priest, the slave, and the liberticide,
Trampled and mocked with many a loathèd rite
  Of lust and blood; he went unterrified
Into the gulf of death; but his clear Sprite
Yet reigns o'er earth, the third among the sons of
      light.

VI

But now thy youngest, dearest one, has perished—
  The nursling of thy widowhood, who grew
Like a pale flower by some sad maiden cherished,
  And fed with true-love tears, instead of dew;
  Most musical of mourners, weep anew!
Thy extreme hope, the loveliest and the last,
  The bloom whose petals, nipt before they blew,
Died on the promise of the fruit, is waste;
The broken lily lies—the storm is overpast.

XXXIX

Peace, peace! he is not dead, he doth not sleep—
  He hath awakened from the dream of life—
'Tis we, who, lost in stormy visions, keep
  With phantoms an unprofitable strife,
  And in mad trance strike with our spirit's knife
Invulnerable nothings. *We* decay
  Like corpses in a charnel; fear and grief
Convulse us and consume us day by day,
And cold hopes swarm like worms within our liv-
      ing clay.

XLII

He is made one with Nature: there is heard
  His voice in all her music, from the moan
Of thunder to the song of night's sweet bird;
  He is a presence to be felt and known
In darkness and in light, from herb and stone,
Spreading itself where'er that Power may move
  Which has withdrawn his being to its own;
Which wields the world with never-wearied love.
Sustains it from beneath, and kindles it above.

XLIII

He is a portion of the loveliness
  Which once he made more lovely; he doth bear
His part, while the one Spirit's plastic stress
  Sweeps through the dull, dense world, compelling
      there
  All new successions to the forms they wear;
Torturing the unwilling dross that checks its flight
  To its own likeness, as each mass may bear,
And bursting in its beauty and its might
From trees and beasts and men into the Heaven's
      light.

XLV

The inheritors of unfulfilled renown
  Rose from their thrones, built beyond mortal
      thought,
Far in the Unapparent. Chatterton
Rose pale—his solemn agony had not
  Yet faded from him; Sidney, as he fought
And as he fell, and as he lived and loved,
  Sublimely mild, a spirit without spot,
Arose; and Lucan, by his death approved;
Oblivion as they rose shrank like a thing reproved.

XLVI

And many more, whose names on earth are dark,
But whose transmitted effluence cannot die
So long as fire outlives the parent spark,
　　Rose, robed in dazzling immortality.
　　"Thou art become as one of us," they cry;
"It was for thee yon kingless sphere has long
　　Swung blind in unascended majesty,
Silent alone amid an Heaven of Song:
Assume thy wingèd throne, thou Vesper of our
　　　　throng!"

LV

The breath whose might I have invoked in song
　　Descends on me; my spirit's bark is driven
Far from the shore, far from the trembling throng
　　Whose sails were never to the tempest given:
　　The massy earth and spherèd skies are riven!
I am borne darkly, fearfully afar;
　　Whilst burning through the inmost veil of Heaven
The soul of Adonais, like a star,
Beacons from the abode where the Eternal are.

THE INDIAN SERENADE

I ARISE from dreams of thee,
　　In the first sweet sleep of night,
When the winds are breathing low,
And the stars are shining bright:
I arise from dreams of thee;
And a spirit in my feet
Has led me—who knows how?—
To thy chamber-window, sweet!

The wandering airs they faint
On the dark, the silent stream;
The champak odors fail,
Like sweet thoughts in a dream.
The nightingale's complaint,
It dies upon her heart,
As I must die on thine,
O belovéd as thou art!

Oh, lift me from the grass!
I die, I faint, I fail.
Let thy love in kisses rain
On my lips and eyelids pale.
My cheek is cold and white, alas!
My heart beats loud and fast.
Oh, press it close to thine again,
Where it will break at last.

GOOD-NIGHT

GOOD-NIGHT? ah, no; the hour is ill
Which severs those it should unite;
Let us remain together still,
Then it will be *good*-night.

How can I call the lone night good,
Though thy sweet wishes wing its flight?
Be it not said, though understood,
Then it will be good-night.

To hearts which near each other move,
From evening close to morning light,
The night is good,—because, my love,
They never *say* good-night.

ON A FADED VIOLET

THE odor from the flower is gone,
　　Which like thy kisses breathed on me;
The color from the flower is flown,
　　Which glowed of thee, and only thee.

A shriveled, lifeless, vacant form,
　　It lies on my abandoned breast,
And mocks the heart which yet is warm,
　　With cold and silent rest.

I weep—my tears revive it not!
　　I sigh—it breathes no more on me!
Its mute and uncomplaining lot
　　Is such as mine should be.

ODE TO LIBERTY

A GLORIOUS people vibrated again
　　The lightning of the nations: Liberty,
From heart to heart, from tower to tower, o'er
　　　　Spain,
　Scattering contagious fire into the sky,
Gleamed.　My Soul spurned the chains of its dis-
　　　　　　may,
　　　　And, in the rapid plumes of song,
　　　　Clothed itself, sublime and strong;

As a young eagle soars the morning clouds among,
　　Hovering in verse o'er its accustomed prey:
　　Till from its station in the heaven of fame
　　The Spirit's whirlwind rapt it, and the ray
　　Of the remotest sphere of living flame
Which paves the void was from behind it flung,

17

As foam from a ship's swiftness, when there
 came
A voice out of the deep: I will record the same.

The Sun and the serenest Moon sprang forth:
 The burning stars of the abyss were hurled
In to the depths of heaven. The dædal earth,
 That island in the ocean of the world,
Hung in its cloud of all-sustaining air.
   But this divinest universe
   Was yet a chaos and a curse,
For thou wert not: but power from worst produc-
  ing worse,
 The spirit of the beasts was kindled there,
  And of the birds, and of the watery forms,
 And there was war among them, and despair
  Within them raging without truce or terms:
The bosom of their violated nurse
 Groan'd, for beasts warr'd on beasts, and worms
  on worms,
And men on men; each heart was as a hell of
 storms.

Man, the imperial shape, then multiplied
 His generations under the pavilion
Of the Sun's throne: palace and pyramid,
 Temple and prison, to many a swarming million
Were as to mountain-wolves their ragged caves.
   This human living multitude
   Was savage, cunning, blind, and rude,
For thou wert not; but o'er the populous solitude,
 Like one fierce cloud over a waste of waves,
  Hung tyranny; beneath, sate deified
 The sister pest, congregator of slaves
  Into the shadow of her pinions wide,
Anarchs and priests who feed on gold and blood,
 Till with the stain their inmost souls are dyed.
 Drove the astonished herds of men from every
 side.

The nodding promontories, and blue isles,
   And cloud-like mountains, and dividuous waves
Of Greece, basked glorious in the open smiles
   Of favoring heaven: from their enchanted caves
Prophetic echoes flung dim melody
        On the unapprehensive wild.
        The vine, the corn, the olive mild,
Grew savage yet, to human use unreconciled;
   And, like unfolded flowers beneath the sea,
     Like the man's thought dark in the infant's
       brain,
     Like aught that is which wraps what is to be,
       Art's deathless dreams lay veiled by many a
       vein
Of Parian stone; and yet a speechless child,
   Verse murmured, and Philosophy did strain
   Her lidless eyes for thee; when o'er the Ægian
     main

Athens arose; a city such as vision
Builds from the purple crags and silver towers
Of battlemented cloud, as in derision
   Of kingliest masonry: the ocean-floors
Pave it; the evening sky pavilions it;
        Its portals are inhabited
        By thunder-zoned winds, each head
Within its cloudy wings with sunfire garlanded,
   A divine work! Athens diviner yet
     Gleamed with its crest of columns, on the will
Of man, as on a mount of diamond, set;
     For thou wert, and thine all-creative skill
Peopled with forms that mock the eternal dead
   In marble immortality, that hill
   Which was thine earliest throne and latest oracle.

Within the surface of Time's fleeting river
   Its wrinkled image lies, as then it lay,
Immovably unquiet, and for éver
   It trembles, but it cannot pass away!

The voices of thy bard and sages thunder
     With an earth-awakening blast
     Through the caverns of the past;
Religion veils her eyes; Oppression shrinks aghast:
  A winged sound of joy, and love, and wonder,
    Which soars where Expectation never flew,
  Rending the veil of space and time asunder!
     One ocean feeds the clouds, and streams, and
       dew,
One sun illumines heaven; one spirit vast
  With life and love makes chaos ever new,
  As Athens doth the world with thy delight renew.

Then Rome was, and from thy deep bosom fairest,
  Like a wolf-cub from a Cadmæan Mænad,
She drew the milk of greatness, though thy dearest
  From that Elysian food was yet unweaned;
And many a deed of terrible uprightness
    By thy sweet love was sanctified;
    And in thy smile, and by thy side,
Saintly Camillus lived and firm Atilius died.
  But when tears stained thy robe of vestal white-
     ness,
    And gold profaned thy capitolian throne,
Thou didst desert, with spirit-winged lightness,
    The senate of the tyrants: they sunk prone,
Slaves of one tyrant: Palatinus sighed
  Faint echoes of Ionian song; that tone
Thou didst delay to hear, lamenting to disown.

A thousand years the Earth cried, Where art thou?
  And then the shadow of thy coming fell
On Saxon Alfred's olive-cinctured brow:
  And many a warrior-peopled citadel,
Like rocks which fire lifts out of the flat deep,
     Arose in sacred Italy,
     Frowning o'er the tempestuous sea

Of kings, and priests, and slaves, in tower-crowned
      majesty;
  That multitudinous anarchy did sweep,
    And burst around their walls, like idle foam,
    Whilst from the human spirit's deepest deep
    Strange melody with love and awe struck dumb
Dissonant arms; and Art, which cannot die,
  With divine want traced on our earthly home
  Fit imagery to pave heaven's everlasting dome.

Thou huntress swifter than the Moon! thou terror
  Of the world's wolves! thou bearer of the quiver,
Whose sunlike shafts pierce tempest-winged Error,
  As light may pierce the clouds when they dissever
In the calm regions of the Orient day!
      Luther caught thy wakening glance,
      Like lightning, from his leaden lance
Reflected, it dissolved the visions of the trance
  In which, as in a tomb the nations lay;
    And England's prophets hailed thee as their
      queen,
  In songs whose music cannot pass away,
    Though it must flow for ever: not unseen
Before the spirit sighted countenance
  Of Milton didst thou pass, from the sad scene
Beyond whose night he saw, with a dejected mien.

The eager hours and unreluctant years
  As on a dawn-illumined mountain stood,
Trampling to silence their loud hopes and fears,
  Darkening each other with their multitude,
And cried aloud, Liberty! Indignation
      Answered Pity from her cave:
      Death grew pale within the grave,
And Desolation howled to the destroyer, Save!
  When like heaven's sun girt by the exhalation
    Of its own glorious light, thou didst arise,
  Chasing thy foes from nation unto nation

Like shadows: as if day had cloven the skies
At dreaming midnight o'er the western wave,
  Men started staggering with a glad surprise,
  Under the lightnings of thine unfamiliar eyes.

Thou heaven of earth! what spells could pall thee
       then,
  In ominous eclipse? a thousand years
Bred from the slime of deep oppression's den,
  Dyed all thy liquid light with blood and tears,
Till thy sweet stars could weep the stain away;
       How like Bacchanals of blood
       Round France, the ghastly vintage, stood
Destruction's sceptered slaves, and Folly's miter'd
       brood!
  When one, like them, but mightier far than they,
    The Anarch of thine own bewildered powers,
  Rose: armies mingled in obscure array,
    Like clouds with clouds, darkening the sacred
      bowers
Of serene heaven. He, by the past pursued,
  Rests with those dead, but unforgotten hours,
  Whose ghosts scare victor kings in their ances-
    tral towers.

England yet sleeps: was she not called of old?
  Spain calls her now, as with its thrilling thunder
Vesuvius wakens Ætna, and the cold
  Snow-crags by its reply are cloven in sunder:
O'er the lit waves every Æolian isle
    From Pithecusa to Pelorus
    Howls, and leaps, and glares in chorus:
They cry, Be dim; ye lamps of heaven suspended
    o'er us.
  Her chains are threads of gold, she need but smile
    And they dissolve; but Spain's were links of
      steel,

Till bit to dust by virtue's keenest file.
    Twins of a single destiny! appeal
To the eternal years enthroned before us,
  In the dim West; impress us from a seal,
  All ye have thought and done! Time cannot dare
      conceal.
Tomb of Arminius! render up thy dead,
  Till, like a standard from a watch-tower's staff,
His soul may stream over the tyrant's head;
  Thy victory shall be his epitaph!
Wild Bacchanal of truth's mysterious wine,
      King-deluded Germany,
        His dèad spirit lives in thee.
Why do we fear or hope? thou art already free!
And thou, lost Paradise of this divine
    And glorious world! thou flowery wilderness!
Thou island of eternity! thou shrine
  Where desolation clothed with loveliness,
Worships the thing thou wert! O Italy,
  Gather thy blood into thy heart; repress
  The beasts who make their dens thy sacred
      palaces.

He who taught man to vanquish whatsoever
  Can be between the cradle and the grave
Crowned him the King of Life. O vain endeavor!
  If on his own high will a willing slave,
He has enthroned the oppression and the oppressor.
    What if earth can clothe and feed
    Amplest millions at their need,
And power in thought be as the tree within the
    seed?
  Or what if Art, an ardent intercessor,
    Driving on fiery wings to Nature's throne,
Checks the great mother stooping to caress her,
  And cries: Give me, thy child, dominion
Over all height and depth? if Life can breed

New wants, and Wealth from those who toil and
    groan
Rend of thy gifts and hers a thousand fold for
    one?

Come Thou, but lead out of the inmost cave
Of man's deep spirit, as the morning-star
Beckons the Sun from the Eoan wave,
    Wisdom. I hear the pennons of her ear
Self-moving, like clouds charioted by flame;
        Comes she not, and come ye not,
        Rulers of eternal thought,
To judge, with solemn truth, life's ill apportioned
    lot?
    Blind Love, and equal Justice, and the Fame
      Of what has been, the Hope of what will be?
    O, Liberty! if such could be thy name
      Wert thou disjoined from these, or they from
        thee:
If thine or theirs were treasures to be bought
    By blood or tears, have not the wise and free
    Wept tears, and blood-like tears? The solemn
      harmony
Paused, and the spirit of that mighty singing
    To its abyss was suddenly withdrawn;
Then, as a wild swan, when sublimely winging
    Its path athwart the thunder-smoke of dawn,
Sinks headlong through the aerial golden light
      On the heavy sounding plain.
      When the bolt has pierced its brain;
As summer clouds dissolve, unburthened of their
    rain;
    As a far taper fades with fading night,
      As a brief insect dies with dying day,
    My song, its pinions disarrayed of might,
      Drooped; o'er it closed the echoes far away
Of the great voice which did its flight sustain,

As waves which lately paved his watery way
Hiss round a drowner's head in their tempestu-
    ous play.

MUSIC, WHEN SOFT VOICES DIE

MUSIC, when soft voices die,
    Vibrates in the memory—
Odors, when sweet violets sicken,
Live within the sense they quicken.

Rose-leaves, when the rose is dead,
Are heap'd for the beloved's bed;
And so thy thoughts, when thou art gone,
Love itself shall slumber on.

R. BRINSLEY SHERIDAN

RICHARD BRINSLEY SHERIDAN, one of the most famous of British dramatists, was born in Dublin in 1751; died in London in 1816. He was educated at Harrow, and studied law at the Middle Temple, London. He was intensely interested in politics, as well as in literature, and as a member of Parliament took a prominent part. His comedies, full of sparkling wit and strong characterization, are still played to appreciative audiences. The best are "The Rivals," "The Critic" and "The School for Scandal."

MRS. MALAPROP

(From "The Rivals," a Comedy)

CHARACTERS

MRS. MALAPROP.

LYDIA LANGUISH, *her ward, too fond of romances.*

SIR ANTHONY ABSOLUTE.

CAPTAIN ABSOLUTE, *his son, who under the name of* BEVERLEY, *has won* LYDIA's *affections.*

SCENE: *A Room in* MRS. MALAPROP's *Lodgings at Bath.* LYDIA, MRS. MALAPROP, *and* SIR ANTHONY ABSOLUTE.

Mrs. Mal. There, Sir Anthony, there sits the deliberate simpleton who wants to disgrace her family, and lavish herself on a fellow not worth a shilling.

Lyd. Madam, I thought you once——

Mrs. Mal. You thought, miss! I don't know any business you have to think at all—thought does not

26

become a young woman. But the point we would request of you is, that you will promise to forget this fellow—to illiterate him, I say, quite from your memory.

Lyd. Ah, madam! our memories are independent of our wills. It is not so easy to forget.

Mrs. Mal. But I say it is, miss; there is nothing on earth so easy as to forget, if a person chooses to set about it. I'm sure I have as much forgot your poor dear uncle as if he had never existed—and I thought it my duty so to do; and let me tell you, Lydia, these violent memories don't become a young woman.

Sir Anth. Why, sure she won't pretend to remember what she's ordered not!—ay, this comes of her reading.

Lyd. What crime, madam, have I committed, to be treated thus?

Mrs. Mal. Now don't attempt to extirpate yourself from the matter; you know I have proof controvertible of it.—But tell me, will you promise to do as you're bid? Will you take a husband of your friends' choosing?

Lyd. Madam, I must tell you plainly, that had I no preference for any one else, the choice you have made would be my aversion.

Mrs. Mal. What business have you, miss, with preference and aversion? They don't become a young woman; and you ought to know, that as both always wear off; 'tis safest in matrimony to begin with a little aversion. I am sure I hated your poor dear uncle before marriage as if he'd been a blacka-moor—and yet, miss, you are sensible what a wife I made!—and when it pleased Heaven to release me from him, 'tis unknown what tears I shed!—But suppose we were going to give you another choice, will you promise us to give up this Beverley?

Lyd. Could I belie my thoughts so far as to give

that promise, my actions would certainly as far belie my words.

Mrs. Mal. Take yourself to your room.—You are
fit company for nothing but your own ill-humors.

Lyd. Willingly, ma'am—I cannot change for the
worse   [*Exit.*

Mrs. Mal. There's a little intricate hussy for
you.

Sir Anth. It is not to be wondered at, ma'am,
—all this is the natural consequence of teaching
girls to read. Had I a thousand daughters, by
Heaven! I'd as soon have them taught the black
art as their alphabet!

Mrs. Mal. Nay, nay, Sir Anthony, you are an absolute misanthropy.

Sir Anth. In my way hither, Mrs. Malaprop, I
observed your niece's maid coming forth from a
circulating library!—She had a book in each hand—
they were half-bound volumes, with marble covers!
—From that moment I guessed how full of duty I
should see her mistress!

Mrs. Mal. Those are vile places, indeed!

Sir Anth. Madam, a circulating library in a town
is an evergreen tree of diabolical knowledge! It
blossoms through the year!—And depend on it, Mrs.
Malaprop, that they who are so fond of handling
the leaves, will long for the fruit at last.

Mrs. Mal. Fy, fy, Sir Anthony, you surely speak
laconically.

Sir Anth. Why, Mrs. Malaprop, in moderation
now, what would you have a woman know?

Mrs. Mal. Observe me, Sir Anthony. I would by
no means wish a daughter of mine to be a progeny
of learning; I don't think so much learning becomes
a young woman; for instance, I would never let
her meddle with Greek, or Hebrew, or algebra, or
simony, or fluxions, or paradoxes, or such inflam-
matory branches of learning—neither would it be

necessary for her to handle any of your mathematical, astronomical, diabolical instruments.—But, Sir Anthony, I would send her, at nine years old, to a boarding-school, in order to learn a little ingenuity and artifice. Then, sir, she should have a supercilious knowledge in accounts;—and as she grew up, I would have her instructed in geometry, that she might know something of the contagious countries;—but, above all, Sir Anthony, she should be mistress of orthodoxy, that she might not misspell and mispronounce words so shamefully as girls usually do; and likewise that she might reprehend the true meaning of what she is saying. This, Sir Anthony, is what I would have a woman know;—and I don't think there is a superstitious article in it.

Sir Anth. Well, well, Mrs. Malaprop, I will dispute the point no further with you; though I must confess, that you are a truly moderate and polite arguer, for almost every third word you say is on my side of the question. But, Mrs. Malaprop, to the more important point in debate—you say you have no objection to my proposal?

Mrs. Mal. None, I assure you. I am under no positive engagement with Mr. Acres, and as Lydia is so obstinate against him, perhaps your son may have better success.

Sir Anth. Well, madam, I will write for the boy directly. He knows not a syllable of this yet, though I have for some time had the proposal in my head. He at present with his regiment.

Mrs. Mal. We have never seen your son, Sir Anthony; but I hope no objection on his side.

Sir Anth. Objection!—let him object if he dare! —No, no, Mrs. Malaprop, Jack knows that the least demur puts me in a frenzy directly. My process was always very simple—in their younger days, 'twas "Jack, do this;"—if he demurred, I knocked him down—and if he grumbled at that, I always sent him out of the room.

Mrs. Mal. Ay, and the properest way, o' my conscience!—nothing is so conciliating to young people, as severity.—Well Sir Anthony, I shall give Mr. Acres his discharge, and prepare Lydia to receive your son's invocations;—and I hope you will represent her to the captain as an object not altogether illegible.

Sir Anth. Madam, I will handle the subject prudently.—Well, I must leave you; and let me beg you, Mrs. Malaprop, to enforce this matter roundly to the girl.—Take my advice—keep a tight hand: if she rejects this proposal, clap her under lock and key; and if you were just to let the servants forget to bring her dinner for three or four days, you can't conceive how she'd come about.

*   *   *   *   *   *   *

SCENE AS BEFORE.

MRS. MALAPROP, *with a letter in her hand, and* CAPTAIN ABSOLUTE.

Mrs. Mal. Your being Sir Anthony's son, captain, would itself be a sufficient accommodation; but from the ingenuity of your appearance, I am convinced you deserve the character here given of you.

Abs. Permit me to say, madam, that as I never yet have had the pleasure of seeing Miss Languish, my principal inducement in this affair at present, is the honor of being allied to Mrs. Malaprop; of whose intellectual accomplishments, elegant manners, and unaffected learning, no tongue is silent.

Mrs. Mal. Sir, you do me infinite honor! I beg, captain, you'll be seated.—[*They sit.*] Ah! few gentlemen, now-a-days, know how to value the ineffectual qualities in a woman! few think how a little knowledge becomes a gentiewoman!—Men have no sense now but for the worthless flower of beauty!

Abs. It is but too true, indeed, ma'am;—yet I fear our ladies should share the blame—they think our admiration of beauty so great, that knowledge in them would be superfluous. Thus, like garden-trees, they seldom show fruit, till time has robbed them of the more specious blossom.—Few, like Mrs. Malaprop and the orange-tree, are rich in both at once!

Mrs. Mal. Sir, you overpower me with good breeding.—He is the very pine-apple of politeness! [*Aside.*]—You are not ignorant, captain, that this giddy girl has somehow contrived to fix her affections on a beggarly, strolling, eavesdropping ensign, whom none of us have seen, and nobody knows anything of.

Abs. Oh, I have heard the silly affair before.—I'm not at all prejudiced against her on that account

Mrs. Mal. You are very good and very considerate, captain. I am sure I have done everything in my power since I exploded the affair; long ago I laid my positive conjunctions on her, never to think on the fellow again:—I have since laid Sir Anthony's preposition before her; but, I am sorry to say, she seems resolved to decline every particle that I enjoin her.

Abs. It must be very distressing, indeed, ma'am.

Mrs. Mal. Oh! it gives me the hydrostatics to such a degree.—I thought she had persisted from corresponding with him; but, behold this very day, I have interceded another letter from the fellow; I believe I have it in my pocket.

Abs. Oh, the devil! my last note. [*Aside.*

Mrs. Mal. Ay, here it is.

Abs. Ay, my note indeed! O the little traitress Lucy. [*Aside.*

31

Mrs. Mal. There, perhaps you may know the writing.   [*Gives him the letter.*

Abs. I think I have seen the hand before—yes, I certainly must have seen this hand before—

Mrs. Mal. Nay, but read it, captain.

Abs [Reads.] *My soul's idol, my adored Lydia!* —Very tender indeed!

Mrs. Mal. Tender! ay, and profane too, o' my conscience.

Abs. [Reads.] *I am excessively alarmed at the intelligence you send me, the more so as my new rival*——

Mrs. Mal. That's you, sir.

Abs. [Reads.] *Has universally the character of being an accomplished gentleman, and a man of honor.*—Well, that's handsome enough.

Mrs. Mal. Oh, the fellow has some design in writing so.

Abs. That he had, I'll answer for him, ma'am.

Mrs. Mal. But go on, sir—you'll see presently.

Abs. [Reads.] *As for the old weather-beaten she-dragon who guards you*—Who can he mean by that?

Mrs. Mal. Me, sir!—me!—he means me!—There— what do you think now?—but go on a little further.

Abs. Impudent scoundrel!—[Reads.] *it shall go hard but I will elude her vigilance, as I am told that the same ridiculous vanity which makes her dress up her coarse features, and deck her dull chat with hard words which she don't understand*——

Mrs Mal. There, sir, an attack upon my language! what do you think of that?—an aspersion upon my parts of speech! was ever such a brute! Sure, if I reprehend anything in this world, it is the use of my oracular tongue, and a nice derangement of epitaphs.

Abs. He deserves to be hanged and quartered! Let me see—[Reads]—*same ridiculous vanity*——

32

Mrs. Mal. You need not read it again, sir.

Abs. I beg pardon, ma'am.—[Reads.] *does also lay er open to the grossest deceptions from flattery and pretended admiration*—an impudent coxcomb!—*so hat I have a scheme to see you shortly with the old arridan's consent, and even to make her a go-etween in our interview.*—Was ever such assurance!

Mrs. Mal. Did you ever hear anything like it?—he'll elude my vigilance, will he—yes, yes! ha! ha! he's very likely to enter these doors;—we will try who can plot best!

Abs. So we will, ma'am—so we will! Ha! ha! ha! a conceited puppy, ha! ha! ha!—Well, but Mrs. Malaprop, as the girl seems so infatuated by this fellow, suppose you were to wink at her corresponding with his for a little time—let her even plot an elopement with him—then do you connive at her escape—while I, just in the nick, will have the fellow laid by the heels, and fairly contrive to carry er off in his stead.

Mrs. Mal. I am delighted with the scheme; never was anything better perpetrated!

Abs. But, pray, could not I see the lady for a few minutes now?—I should like to try her temper a little.

Mrs. Mal. Why, I don't know—I doubt she is not prepared for a visit of this kind. There is a decorum in these matters.

Abs. O Lord! she won't mind me—only tell her Beverley——

Mrs. Mal. Sir!

Abs. Gently, good tongue   [*Aside.*

Mrs. Mal. What did you say of Beverley?

Abs. Oh, I was going to propose that you should tell her, by way of jest, that it was Beverley who is below; she'd come down fast enough then—ha! ha!

Mrs. Mal. 'Twould be a trick she well deserves;

besides you know the fellow tells her he'll get m[
consent to see her—ha! ha! Let him if he can, I sa[
again. Lydia, come down here!—[*Calling.*] He'[
make me a go-between in their interviews!—ha! ha[
ha! Come down, I say, Lydia! I don't wonder a[
your laughing, ha! ha! ha! his impudence is trul[
ridiculous.

Abs. 'Tis very ridiculous, upon my soul, ma'an[
ha! ha! ha!

Mrs. Mal. The little hussy won't hear. Well, I'[
go and tell her at once who it is—she shall know tha[
Captain Absolute is come to wait on her. And I'[
make her behave as becomes a young woman.

Abs. As you please, ma'am.

Mrs. Mal. For the present, captain, your servan[
Ah! you've not done laughing yet, I see—elude m[
vigilance; yes, yes; ha! ha! ha!   [*Exi[*

Abs. Ha! ha! ha! one would think now that[
might throw off all disguise at once, and seize m[
prize with security; but such is Lydia's caprice, tha[
to undeceive were probably to lose her. I'll s[
whether she knows me.

[*Walks aside, and seems engaged in looking [
the pictures.*

Enter LYDIA.

Lyd. What a scene am I now to go through! sur[
ly nothing can be more dreadful than to be oblige[
to listen to the loathsome addresses of a stranger t[
one's heart. I have heard of girls persecuted as [
am, who have appealed in behalf of their favore[
lover to the generosity of his rival; suppose I we[
to try it—there stands the hated rival—an office[
too!—but, oh, how unlike my Beverley! I wond[
he don't begin—truly he seems a very neglige[
wooer!—quite a this ease, upon my word!—I'll spe[
first—Mr. Absolute.

Abs. Ma'am!   [*Turns roun[*

Lyd. O Heavens! Beverley!

Abs. Hush! hush, my life! softly! be not surprised!

Lyd. I am so astonished! and so terrified! and so overjoyed!—for Heaven's sake! how came you here?

Abs. Briefly, I have deceived your aunt—I was informed that my new rival was to visit here this evening, and contriving to have him kept away, have passed myself on her for Captain Absolute.

Lyd. O charming! And she really takes you for young Absolute?

Abs. Oh, she's convinced of it.

Lyd. Ha! ha! ha! I can't forbear laughing to think how her sagacity is overreached.

Abs. But we trifle with our precious moments—such another opportunity may not occur; then let me now conjure my kind, my condescending angel, to fix the time when I may rescue her from undeserving persecution, and with a licensed warmth plead for my reward.

Lyd. Will you then, Beverley, consent to forfeit that portion of my paltry wealth?—that burden on the wings of love?

Abs. Oh, come to me—rich only thus—in loveliness! Bring no portion to me but thy love—'twill be generous in you, Lydia—for well you know, it is the only dower your poor Beverley can repay.

Lyd. How persuasive are his words!—how charming will poverty be with him!   [*Aside.*

Abs. Ah! my soul, what a life will we then live! Love shall be our idol and support! we will worship him with a monastic strictness; abjuring all worldly joys, to center every thought and action there. Proud of calamity, we will enjoy the wreck of wealth; while the surrounding gloom of adversity shall make the flame of our pure love show doubly bright.

B. P. SHILLABER

Benjamin Penhallow Shillaber, an American humorist, was born in Portsmouth, N. H., in 1814; died at Chelsea, Mass., in 1890. He attended a district school for a while and then entered a printing office. His writings attracted more than local attention and in 1840 he became editor of the Boston *Post*. From 1856 to 1866 he had charge of the *Saturday Evening Gazette*. His "Life and Sayings of Mrs. Partington" have placed him in the front rank of American humorists.

MRS. PARTINGTON'S SAYINGS

DEAR me! here they are going to have war again over the sea, and only for a Turkey, and it don't say how much it weighed either, nor whether it was tender; and Prince Knockemstiff has gone off in a miff, and the Rushian bears and austriches are all to be let loose to devour the people and heaven knows where the end of it will leave off War is a dreadful thing—so destroying to good temper and good clo'es, and men shoot at each other just as if they was gutter purchase, and cheap at that."

"What is your opinion of the humor of Hawthorne, Mrs. Partington?" asked a young neighbor that had been reading "Twice-Told Tales." "I don' know," said she, looking at him earnestly; "but i you have got it, you'd better take something to kee it from striking in. Syrup of buckthorn is good fo all sorts of diseases of that kind; I don't know about the humor of Hawthorne, but I guess th buckthorne will be beneficious. We eat too much butter, and butter is very humorous."

"It is all very true, Mr. Knickerbottom," said Mrs. Partington, as she read in the Knickerbocker something concerning brevity and simplicity of expression; "it's true, as you say; and how many mistakes there does happen when folks don't understand each other! Why, last summer I told a dressmaker to make me a long visite, to wear, and would you believe it, she came and stayed a fortnight with me! Since then I've made it a pint always to speak just what I say."

"I never liked the Swedenvirgins; but I ain't one of that believes nothing good can come out of Lazarus, for all that now. Now, there's Jenny Lind —that is so very good to everybody, and who sings so sweet that everybody's falling in love with her, tipsy-turvy, and gives so much away to poor, indignant people. They call her an angel, and who knows but she may be a syrup in disguise, for the papers say her singing is like the music of the spears. How I should love to hear her!"

"A knave in our church! Who can it be? Dear me, and they have been so careful, too, who they took in—exercising 'em aforehand, and putting 'em through the catechis and the lethargy, and pounding 'em into a state of grace! Who can it be?" And the spectacles expressed anxiety. "I believe it must be slander after all. Oh, what a terrible thing it is to pisen the peace of a neighborhood deteriorating and backbiting, and lying about people, when the blessed truth is full bad enough about the best of us!"

"Entered at the Custom House?" said Mrs. Partington, pondering on the expression; "I don't see how the vessels ever got in; but I am glad that the collector cleared 'em right out again. It will learn them better manners next time, I think."

37

Deacon Snarl, in exhortation, would often allude to the "place where prayer is wont to be made." "Ah!" said Mrs. Partington to herself, "there's nothing like humility in a Christian. I am glad you confess it. I don't know a place under the canister of heaven where prayer is wanted more to be made than here, and I hope you'll be forgiven for the rancorous butter you sold me yesterday."

Mrs. Partington's neighbor, Mrs. Sled, complained one morning of a ringing in her ears. "It must be owing to the guitar in your head, dear," said the old lady. She knew every sort of human ailment, and, like the down-east doctor, was death on fits. "I know what ringing in the ears is," continued she; "for my ears used to ring so bad, sometimes, as to wake Paul out of his sleep, thinking it was an alarm of fire!"

"The prayer of Moses executed on one string!" said Mrs. Partington. "Praying, I s'pose, to be cut down. Poor Moses!" sighed she; "executed on one string! Well, I don't know as ever I heard of anybody's being executed on two strings, unless the rope broke;" and she went on wondering how it could be.

MRS. PARTINGTON IN COURT

"I TOOK my knitting-work and went up into the gallery," said Mrs. Partington, the day after visiting one of the city courts; "I went up into the gallery, and after I had adjusted my specs, I looked down into the room, but I couldn't see any courting going on. An old gentleman seemed to be asking a good many impertinent questions—just like some old folks—and people were sitting around making minutes of the conversation. I don't see how they made out what was said, for they all told different stories. How much easier it would be to get along if they were all made to tell the same story! What a sight of trouble it would save the lawyers! The case, as they call it, was given to the jury, but I couldn't see it, and a gentleman with a long pole was made to swear that he'd keep an eye on 'em, and see that they didn't run away with it. Bimeby in they came again, and they said somebody was guilty of something, who had just said he was innocent, and didn't know nothing about it no more than the little baby that had never subsistence. I come away soon afterward; but I couldn't help thinking how trying it must be to sit there all day, shut out from the blessed air!"

SYDNEY SMITH

Sydney Smith, clergyman and essayist, was born in Woodford, Essex, England, in 1771; died in London in 1845. He was educated at Oxford, and became a curate and later went to Edinburgh to edit the Edinburgh *Review*. In 1831 he was made a canon of St. Paul's, London. His letters and philosophical writings are models of style, and throughout can be found those humorous touches that counted him one of the brightest wits of his day.

MAKING HASTE SLOWLY

(From "Moral Philosophy")

THERE is something extremely fascinating in quickness; and most men are desirous of appearing quick. The great rule for becoming so is, *by not attempting to appear quicker than you really are;* by resolving to understand yourself and others, and to know what *you* mean, and what *they* mean, before you speak or answer. Every man must submit to be slow before he is quick; and insignificant before he is important. The too early struggle against the pain of obscurity corrupts no small share of understandings. Well and happily has that man conducted his understanding who has learned to derive from the exercise of it regular occupation and rational delight; who, after having overcome the first pain of application, and acquired a habit of looking inwardly upon his own mind, perceives that every day is multiplying the relations, confirming the accuracy, and augmenting the number of his ideas; who feels that he is rising in the scale of intellectual beings, gathering new strength with every new difficulty which he subdues, and enjoying to-day as his pleasure that which yesterday he labored at as his toil. There are many consolations in the mind of such a man which no common life can ever afford, and many enjoyments which it has not to give! It is not the mere cry of moralists, and the flourish of rhetoricians; but it is *noble* to seek truth, and it is *beautiful* to find it. It is the ancient feeling of the human heart,—that knowledge is better than riches; and it is deeply and *sacredly true!*

To mark the course of human passions as they have flowed on in the ages that are past; to see why nations have risen, and why they have fallen; to speak of heat, and light, and winds; to know what man has discovered in the heavens above, and in the earth beneath; to hear the chemist unfold the marvelous properties that the Creator has locked up in a speck of earth; to be told that there are worlds so distant from our sun that the quickness of light traveling from the world's creation has never yet reached us; to wander in the creations of poetry, and grow warm again, with that eloquence which swayed the democracies of the old world; to go up with great reasoners to the First Cause of all, and to perceive in the midst of all this dissolution and decay, and cruel separation, that there *is* one thing unchangeable, indestructible, and everlasting;—it is worth while in the days of our youth to strive hard for this great discipline; to pass sleepless nights for it, to give up to it laborious days; to spurn for it present pleasures; to endure for it afflicting poverty; to wade for it through darkness, and sorrow, and contempt, as the great spirits of the world have done in all ages and all times.

41

A RECEIPT FOR SALAD

TO make this condiment your poet begs
   The pounded yellow of two hard-boiled eggs;
Two boiled potatoes, passed through kitchen sieve,
Smoothness and softness to the salad give;
Let onion atoms lurk within the bowl,
And, half suspected, animate the whole;
Of mordant mustard add a single spoon,
Distrust the condiment that bites too soon;
But deem it not, thou man of herbs, a fault
To add a double quantity of salt;
Four times the spoon with oil from Lucca crown,
And twice with vinegar, procured from town;
And lastly, o'er the flavored compound toss
A magic soupçon of anchovy sauce.
O green and glorious! O herbaceous treat!
'Twould tempt the dying anchorite to eat;
Back to the world he'd turn his fleeting soul,
And plunge his fingers in the salad-bowl;
Serenely full, the epicure would say,
"Fate cannot harm me—I have dined to-day."

WIT

THERE is an association in men's minds between
   dulness and wisdom, amusement and folly,
which has a very powerful influence in decision upon
character, and is not overcome without considerable
difficulty. The reason is, that the *outward* signs of
a dull man and a wise man are the same, and so are
the outward signs of a frivolous man and a witty
man; and we are not to expect that the majority
will be disposed to look to much *more* than the outward sign. I believe the fact to be that wit is very
seldom the *only* eminent quality which resides in the
mind of any man; it is commonly accompanied by

many other talents of every description, and ought
to be considered as a strong evidence of a fertile
and superior understanding. Almost all the great
poets, orators, and statesmen of all times, have been
witty, Cæsar, Alexander, Aristotle, Descartes, and
Lord Bacon, were witty men; so were Cicero,
Shakespeare, Demosthenes, Boileau, Pope, Dryden,
Fontenelle, Jonson, Waller, Cowley, Solon, Socrates,
Dr. Johnson, and almost every man who has made a
distinguished figure in the House of Commons.
. . . The meaning of an extraordinary man is, that
he is *eight* men, not one man; that he has as much
wit as if he had no sense, and as much sense as
if he had no wit; that his conduct is as judicious
as if he were the dullest of human beings, and his
imagination as brilliant as if he were irretrievably
ruined. But when wit is combined with sense and
information; when it is softened by benevolence,
and restrained by strong principle; when it is in the
hands of a man who can use it and despise it, who
can be witty, and sometimes much *better* than witty,
who loves honor, justice, decency, good-nature, mor-
ality and religion, ten thousand times better than
wit;—wit is *then* a beautiful and delightful part of
our nature. There is no more interesting spectacle
than to see the effects of wit upon the different characters of men; than to observe it expanding caution,
relaxing dignity, unfreezing coldness—teaching age,
and care, and pain, to smile—extorting reluctant
gleams of pleasure from melancholy, and charming
even the pangs of grief. It is pleasant to observe
how it penetrates through the coldness and awkward-
ness of society, gradually bringing men nearer together, and, like the combined force of wine and
oil, giving every man a glad heart and a shining
countenance. Genuine and innocent wit like this is
surely the *flavor of the mind!* Man could direct his
way by plain reason, and support his life by taste-

less food; but God has given us wit, and flavor, and laughter, and perfumes, to enliven the days of man's pilgrimage, and to " charm his pained steps over the burning marle."

TOO MUCH LATIN AND GREEK
(From Edinburg Review, Oct., 1809)

THAT vast advantages, then, may be derived from classical learning, there can be no doubt. The advantages which are derived from classical learning by the English manner of teaching involve another and a very different question; and we will venture to say, that there never was a more complete instance in any country of such extravagant and overacted attachment to any branch of knowledge as that which obtains in this country with regard to classical knowledge. A young gentleman goes to school at six or seven years old; and he remains in a course of education till twenty-three or twenty-four years of age. In all that time his sole and exclusive occupation is learning Latin and Greek (unless he goes to the University of Cambridge); and then classics occupy him entirely for about ten years: and divide him with mathematics for four or five more: *foot-note*): he has scarcely a notion that there is any other kind of excellence. These facts the English youth get by heart the moment they quit the nursery; and are most sedulously and industriously instructed in them till the best and most active part of life is passed away. Now, this long career of classical learning, we may, if we please, denominate a foundation; but it is a foundation so far above ground, that there is absolutely no room to put anything upon it. If you occupy a man with one thing till he is twenty-four years of age, you have exhausted all his leisure time: he is called into the world and compelled to act; or is surrounded with pleasures and thinks and reads no more. If you have neglected to put other things in him, they will never get in afterwards;—if you have fed him only with words, he will remain a narrow and limited being to the end of his existence.

The bias given to men's minds is so strong that it is no uncommon thing to meet with Englishmen whom, but for their gray hairs and wrinkles, we might easily mistake for school-boys. Their talk is of Latin verses; and it is quite clear, if men's ages are to be dated from the state of their mental progress, that such men are eighteen years of age, and not a day older. Their minds have been so completely possessed by exaggerated notions of classical learning that they have not been able, in the great school of the world, to form any other notion of real greatness. Attend, too, to the public feelings,—look to all the terms of applause. A learned man! —a scholar!—a man of erudition! Upon whom are these epithets of approbation bestowed? Are they given to men acquainted wtih the science of government? thoroughly masters of the geographical and commercial relations of Europe? to men who know the properties of bodies, and their action upon each other? No: this is not learning; it is chemistry or political economy,—not learning. The distinguishing abstract term, the epithet of Scholar, is reserved for him who writes on the Æolic reduplication, and is familiar with the Sylburgian method of arranging defectives. The picture which a young Englishman, addicted to the pursuit of knowledge, draws,—his *beau ideal* of human nature—his top and consummation of man's powers, is a knowledge of the Greek language. His object is not to reason, to imagine, or to invent; but to conjugate, decline and derive. The situations of imaginary glory which

he draws for himself are the detection of an ana-
pæst in the wrong place, or the restoration of a
dative case which Cranzius had passed over, and the
never-dying Ernesti failed to observe. If a young
classic of this kind were to meet the greatest chemist, or the greatest mechanician, or the most profound political economist, of his time, in company
with the greatest Greek scholar, would the slightest
comparison between them ever come across his mind?
—would he ever dream that such men as Adam Smith
and Lavoisier were equal in dignity of understanding
to, or of the same utility as, Bentley and Heyne?
We are inclined to think that the feeling excited
would be a good deal like that which was expressed
by Dr. George about the praises of the great King
of Prussia, who entertained considerable doubts
whether the King, with all his victories, knew how
to conjugate a Greek verb.

MRS. SIDDONS

I NEVER go to tragedies: my heart is too soft.
There is too much real misery in life. But what
a face she had! The gods do not bestow such a
face as Mrs. Siddons's on the stage more than once
in a century. I knew her very well, and she has
the good taste to laugh heartily at my jokes; she
was an excellent person, but she was not remarkable
out of her profession, and never got out of tragedy
even in common life. She used to *stab* the potatoes;
and said, " Boy, give me a knife! " as she would have
said, " Give me the dagger! "

46

TOBIAS GEORGE SMOLLETT

TOBIAS GEORGE SMOLLETT, Scotch novelist and historian, was born at Dalquhurn, Dumbartonshire, Scotland, in 1721; died in Italy, in 1771. He belonged to an ancient family that had made a name for itself in the annals of his country. He was educated as a surgeon, but preferred writing. His works include travels, poems, novels and histories. His most famous books are "The Adventures of Roderick Random," "The Adventures of an Atom" and "The Expedition of Humphrey Clinker."

THE DOCTOR'S CLASSICAL DINNER

(From "Peregrine Pickle")

PEREGRINE PICKLE, by his insinuating behavior, acquired the full confidence of the Doctor; who invited him to an entertainment which he intended to prepare in the manner of the ancients. Pickle, struck with this idea, eagerly embraced the proposal, which he honored with many encomiums, as a plan in all respects worthy of his genius and apprehension; and the day was appointed at some distance of time, that the treater might have leisure to compose certain pickles and confections which were not to be found among the culinary preparations of these degenerate days. With a view of rendering the physician's taste more conspicuous, and extracting from it the more diversion, Peregrine proposed that some foreigners should partake of the banquet; and the task being left to his care and discretion, he actually bespoke the company of a French Marquis, an Italian Count, and a

German Baron, whom he knew to be egregious cox-combs.

The mutual compliments that passed on this occasion were scarce finished, when a servant, coming into the room, announced dinner; and the entertainer led the way into another apartment, where they found a long table—or rather two boards joined together—and furnished with a variety of dishes, the steams of which had such evident effect upon the nerves of the company, that the Marquis made frightful grimaces under pretence of taking snuff, the Italian's eyes watered, the German's visage underwent several distortions of feature. Our hero found means to exclude the odor from his sense of smelling by breathing only through his mouth; and the poor painter, running into another room, plugged his nostrils with tobacco.

The Doctor himself, who was the only person then present whose organs were not discomposed, pointing to a couple of couches placed on each side of the table, told his guests that he was sorry he could not procure the exact *triclinia* of the ancients, which were somewhat different from these conveniences, and desired that they would have the goodness to repose themselves without ceremony, each in his respective couchette, while he and his friend Mr. Pallet would place themselves upright at the ends, that they might have the pleasure of serving those that lay along. This disposition, of which the strangers had no previous idea, disconcerted and perplexed them in a most ridiculous manner. The Marquis and Baron stood bowing to each other on pretence of disputing the lower seat: but, in reality, with a view of profiting by the example of the other, for neither of them understood the manner in which they were to loll. In this disagreeable and ludicrous suspense they continued acting a pantomime of gesticulations, until the Doctor earnestly entreated them to waive all compliment and form, lest the dinner should be spoiled before the ceremonial could be concluded.

This misfortune being repaired as well as the circumstances of the occasion would permit, and everyone settled according to the arrangement which had been made, the Doctor graciously undertook to give some account of the dishes as they occurred, that the company might be directed in their choice; and with an air of infinite satisfaction, thus began:

"This here, gentlemen, is a boiled goose, served up in a sauce composed of pepper, lovage, coriander, mint, rues, anchovies, and oil. I wish, for your sakes, gentlemen, it was one of the geese of Ferrara, so much celebrated for the magnitude of their livers, one of which is said to have weighed two pounds. With this food, exquisite as it was, did the tyrant Heliogabalus regale his hounds. But I beg pardon; I had almost forgot the soup, which I hear is so necessary at all tables in France. At each end are dishes of the *salacacabia* of the Romans. One is made of parsley, pennyroyal, cheese, pine-tops, honey, vinegar, brine, eggs, cucumbers, onions, and hen-livers; the other is much the same as the *soup-maigro* of this country. Then there is a loin of boiled veal with fennel and caraway-seed, on a pottage composed of pickle, oil, honey and flour; and a curious hashis of the lights, liver and blood of a hare, together with a dish of roasted pigeons. Monsieur le Baron, shall I help you to a plate of this soup?"

The German, who did not at all disapprove of the ingredients, assented to the proposal, and seemed to relish the composition; while the Marquis, being asked by the painter which of the silly-kickabys he chose, was, in consequence of his desire, accommodated with a portion of the *soup-maigre;* and the Count, in lieu of spoon-meat, of which he said he was no great admirer, supplied himself with a pigeon;

therein conforming to the choice of our young
gentlemen, whose example he determined to follow
through the whole course of the entertainment.

*   *   *   *   *   *   *

The Doctor, finding that it would be impracticable
to re-establish the order of the banquet by present-
ing again the dishes which had been discomposed,
ordered everything to be removed, a clean cloth to
be laid, and the dessert to be brought in. Meanwhile he regretted his incapacity to give them a
specimen of the *alicus,* or fish-meals of the ancients:
such as the jusdia-baton, the conger-eel, which, in
Galen's opinion, is hard of digestion; the cornuta,
or gurnard, described by Pliny in his *Natural History,* who says that the horns of many of them were
a foot and a half in length; the mullet and the
lamprey, that were in the highest estimation of old,
of which Julius Cæsar borrowed six thousand for
one triumphal supper. He observed that the manner of dressing them was described by Horace in the
account he gives of the entertainment to which
Mæcenas was invited by the epicure Nasiedenus; and
told them that they were commonly eaten with the
Chus syriacum—a certain anodyne and astringent
seed which qualified the purgative nature of the fish.

Finally this learned physician gave them to understand that though this was reckoned a luxurious dish
in the zenith of the Roman taste, it was by no means
comparable in point of expense to some preparations
in vogue about the time of that absurd voluptuary
Heliogabalus, who ordered the brains of six hundred ostriches to be compounded in one mess.

SOCRATES

SOCRATES, Greek philosopher, was born in Athens, in 470 B.C.; died there in 399 B.C. He was trained as a sculptor, but gave up art to teach ethics, in response to what he believed to be a divine call. In his old age he opposed the party in power in Athens, and was condemned to drink the poisonous "hemlock." His method of teaching was conversational, and in his early years he would go from shop to shop, talking on his favorite themes.

THE PROBLEM OF LIFE AND DEATH

(Translated by Jowett)

FRIENDS, who would have acquitted me, I would like to talk with you about this thing which has happened, before I go to the place at which I must die. Stay then awhile, for we may as well talk with one another while there is time. You are my friends, and I should like to show you the meaning of this event which has happened to me. O my judges—for so I may truly call you, I should like to tell you of a wonderful circumstance:

Hithero the familiar oracle within me has constantly been in the habit of opposing me, even in trifles, if I was going to make a slip or err in any matter; and now, as you see, there has come upon me the last and worst evil. But the oracle made no sign of opposition, either as I was leaving my house and going out in the morning, or while I was speaking, at anything which I was going to say; and yet I have often been stopped in the middle of a speech;

but now in nothing that I either said or did touching this matter has the oracle opposed me. What do I take to be the explanation of this? I will tell you. I regard this as a great proof that what has happened to me is a good; and that those who think that death is an evil are in error. For the customary sign would surely have opposed me had I been going to evil and not to good.

Let us reflect in another way, and we shall see that there is no great reason to hope that death is a good. For one of two things—either death is a state of nothingness; or, as men say, there is a change and migration of the soul from this world to another.

Now if you suppose that there is no consciousness, but a sleep like the sleep of him who is undisturbed even by the sight of dreams, death will be an unspeakable gain. For if a person were to select the night in which his sleep was undisturbed even by dreams, and were to compare this with the other days and nights of his life; and then were to tell us how many days and nights he had passed in the course of his life better and more pleasantly than this one, I think this man—I will not say a private man, but even the great king—will not find many such days or nights, when compared with others. Now if death is like this I say that to die is gain; for eternity is then only a single night.

But if death is the journey to another place—and there, as men say, all the dead are—what good can be greater than this? If, indeed, when the pilgrim arrives in the world below, he is delivered from the professors of justice in this world, and finds the true judges who are said to give judgment there—Minos, and Rhadamanthus, and Æacus, and Triptolemus, and other sons of God who were righteous in their own life—that pilgrimage will be worth making.

Above all, I shall then be able to continue my search into true and false knowledge, as in this world, so also in that. And I shall find out who is wise, and who pretends to be wise and is not. What would not a man give to be able to examine the leader of the Trojan expedition; or Odysseus, or Sisyphus, or numberless others—men and women, too! What infinite delight would there be in conversing with them and asking questions!—in another world they do not put a man to death for asking questions; assuredly not. For besides being happier in that world than in this, they will be immortal, if what is said be true. Wherefore, be of good cheer about death, and know of a certainty that no evil can happen to a good man, either in this life or after death. He and his are not neglected by the gods, nor has my own approaching end happened by mere chance. But I see clearly that to die and be released was better for me; and therefore the oracle gave no sign.

For which reason, also, I am not angry with my condemners or with my accusers. They have done me no harm, although they did not mean to do me any good; and for this I may gently blame them. Still I have a favor to ask of them. When my sons grow up, I would ask you, my friends, to punish them. And I would have you trouble them, as I have troubled you, if they seem to care about riches, or anything more than about virtue. Or of they pretend to be something when they are really nothing, then reprove them, as I have reproved you, for not caring about that for which they ought to care, and thinking that they are really something when they are really nothing. And if you do this, I and my sons will have received justice at your hands.

The hour of my departure has arrived, and we go our ways—I to die, and you to live. Which is better, God only knows.

SOPHOCLES

Sophocles, a Greek dramatic poet, born in Colonus, near Athens, in 496 B.C.; died in 405 B.C. At the age of twenty-six he won the dramatic prize given at the festival of Bacchus. He gave his plays at this festival for forty years, winning either the first, or second place. He wrote over a hundred plays, but only seven are preserved.

THE CHARIOT-RACE

(From "Electra." Translated by Lord Byron)

THEY took their stand where the appointed judges
Had cast their lots and ranged the rival cars,
Rang out the brazen trump! Away they bound,
Cheer the hot steeds, and shake the slackened reins;
As with a body the large space is filled
With the huge clangor of the battling cars.
High whirl aloft the dust-clouds: blent together,
Each presses each, and the lash rings: and loud
Snort the wild steeds, and from their fiery breath
Along their manes and down the circling wheels
Scatter the foam. . . .
       . . . Then order changed to ruin;
Car crashed on car; the wide Circæan plain
was sea-like strewer with wrecks. The Athenian saw,
Slackened his speed, and wheeling round the marge,
Left the wild tumult of that tossing storm.
Behind, Orestes, hitherto the last,
Had yet kept back his courses for the close.
Now one sole rival left, on, on he flew,

And the sharp sound of the impelling scourge
Rang in the keen ears of the flying steeds.
He hears, he reaches; they are side by side;
Now one—the other—by a length the victor.
The courses all are past—the wheels erect—
All safe; when, as the hurrying courses round
The fatal pillar dashed, the wretched boy
Slackened the left rein; on the column's edge
Crashed the frail axle; headlong from the car,
Caught, and all meshed within the reins he fell;
And masterless the mad steeds raged along.

 Loud from that mighty multitude arose
A shriek—a shout! But yesterday such deeds,
To-day such doom! Now whirled upon the earth,
Now his limbs dashed aloft, they dragged him—
  those
Wild horses—till all gory from the wheels
Released: and no man, not his nearest friend,
Could in that mangled corpse have traced Orestes.
They laid the body on the funeral pyre;
And, while we speak, the Phocian strangers bear,
In a small, brazen, melancholy urn,
That handful of cold ashes to which all
The grandeur of the Beautiful hath shrunk.
Hither they bear him, in his father's land
To find that heritage—a tomb!

ROBERT SOUTHEY

ROBERT SOUTHEY, poet, historian, translator and biographer, was born in Bristol, England in 1774; died in Keswick in 1843. In 1795 he wrote an epic, "Joan of Arc." Later he traveled; lived in Portugal; and finally took up his residence in the Lake Region, and with Wordsworth and Coleridge, was classed as one of "The Lake Poets." He was made Poet Laureate in 1813. Although a poet he is perhaps best known by his life of Nelson. Although famed for his poetry he was equally famous as a writer of prose. His histories and biographies are more admired by some critics than are his poems.

NELSON AT THE BATTLE OF THE NILE

(From "The Life of Nelson")

THE first two ships of the French line had been dismasted within a quarter of an hour after the commencement of the action; and the others in that time suffered so severely that victory was already certain. The third, fourth, and fifth were taken possession of at half-past eight. Meantime Nelson received a severe wound on the head from a piece of langrage shot. Captain Perry caught him in his arms as he was falling. The great effusion of blood occasioned an apprehension that the wound was mortal. Nelson himself thought so; a large flap of the skin of the forehead, cut from the bone, had fallen over the eye; and the other being blind, he was in total darkness. When he was carried down, the surgeon, in the midst of a scene scarcely to be conceived by those who have never seen a cockpit in time of action, and the heroism which is displayed amid its horrors, with a natural but pardonable eagerness, quitted the poor fellow then under his hands, that he might instantly attend the admiral. "No!" said Nelson, "I will take my turn with my brave fellows." Nor would he suffer his own wound to be examined till every man who had been previously wounded was properly attended to. Fully believing that the wound was mortal, and that he was about to die, as he had ever desired, in battle and in victory, he called the chaplain, and desired him to deliver what he supposed to be his dying remembrance to Lady Nelson; he then sent for Captain Louis on board from the Minotaur, that he might thank him personally for the great assistance he had rendered to the Vanguard; and, ever mindful of those who deserved to be his friends, appointed Captain Hardy from the brig to the command of his own ship, Captain Perry having to go home with the news of the victory. When the surgeon came in due time to examine the wound (for it was in vain to entreat him to let it be examined sooner), the most anxious silence prevailed; and the joy of the wounded men, and of the whole crew, when they heard that the wound was superficial, gave Nelson deeper pleasure than the unexpected assurance that his life was in no danger. The surgeon requested, and, as far as he could, ordered him to remain quiet; but Nelson could not rest. He called for his secretary, Mr. Campbell, to write the despatches. Campbell had himself been wounded, and was so affected by the blind and suffering state of the admiral that he was unable to write. The chaplain was sent for; but before he came, Nelson, with his characteristic eagerness, took the pen, and contrived to trace a few words, marking his devout sense of the success which had already been obtained. He was now left alone; when suddenly a cry was heard that the *Orient* was on fire. In the confusion he found his way up, unassisted and unnoticed; and to the astonishment of every one, appeared on the quarter-deck, where he immediately gave orders that boats should be sent to the relief of the enemy.

It was soon after nine that the fire on board the *Orient* broke out. Brueys was dead: he had received three wounds, yet would not leave his post. A fourth cut him almost in two. He desired not to be carried below, but to be left to die upon deck. The flames soon masterd his ship. Her sides had just been painted, and the oil-jars and painting-buckets were lying on the poop. By the prodigious light of this conflagration the situation of the two fleets could now be percived, the colors of both being clearly distinguishable. About ten o'clock the ship blew up, with a shock which was felt to the very bottom of every vessel. Many of her officers and men jumped overboard, some clinging to the spars and pieces of wreck with which the sea was strewn; others swimming to escape from the destruction which they momentarily dreaded. Some were picked up by our boats; and some, even in the heat and fury of the action, were dragged into the lower ports of the nearest British ships by the British sailors. The greater part of her crew, however, stood the danger to the last, and continued to fire from the lower deck. This tremendous explosion was followed by a silence not less awful: the firing immediately ceased on both sides; and the first sound which broke the silence was the dash of her shattered masts and yards falling into the water from the vast height to which they had been exploded. It is upon record that a battle between two armies was once broken off by an earthquake;—such an event would be felt like a miracle: but no incident in war, produced by human means, has ever equalled the sublimity of this co-instantaneous pause, and all its circumstances.

About seventy of the *Orient's* crew were saved by the English boats. Among the many hundreds who perished were the commodore, Casa Bianca, and his son, a brave boy only ten years old. They were seen floating on a shattered mast when the boat blew up. She had money on board (the plunder of Malta) to the amount of six hundred thousand pounds sterling. The masses of burning wreck which were scattered by the explosion excited for some moments apprehensions in the English which they had never felt from any other danger. Two large pieces fell into the main and foretops of the *Swiftsure,* without injuring any person. A port-fire also fell into the main-royal of the *Alexander;* the fire which it occasioned was speedily extinguishd. Captain Ball had provided, as far as human foresight could provide, against any such danger. All the shrouds and sails of his ship not absolutely necessary for its immediate management were thoroughly wetted, and so rolled up that they were as hard and as little inflammable as so many solid cylinders.

The firing recommenced with the ships to leeward of the center, and continued till about three. At daybreak the *Guillaume Tell* and the *Généreuse,* the two rears of the enemy, were the only French ships of the line which had their colors flying; they cut their cables in the forenoon, not having been engaged, and stood out to sea, and two frigates with them. The *Zealous* pursued; but, as there was no other ship in a condition to support Captain Hood, he was recalled. It was generally believed by the officers that if Nelson had not been wounded, not one of these ships could have escaped; the four certainly could not, if the *Culloden* had got into action; and if the frigates belonging to the squadron had been present, not one of the enemy's fleet would have left Aboukir Bay. These four vessels, however, were all that escaped; and the victory was the most complete and glorious in the annals of naval victory. "Victory," said Nelson, "is not a name strong enough for such a scene;"—he called it a conquest. Of thirteen sail of the line, nine were taken and two burnt; of the four frigates, one was sunk; another, the *Artemesie*, was burnt in a villanous manner by her captain, M. Estandlet, who, having fired a broadside at the *Thesus*, struck his colors, then set fire to the ship, and escaped with most of his crew to shore. The British loss, in killed and wounded, amounted to 895. Westcott was the only captain who fell: 3105 of the French, including the wounded, were sent on shore by cartel, and 5225 perished.

Thus ended this eventful battle, which exalted the name of Nelson to a level at least with that of the celebrated conqueror whose surprising success at the head of the French armies had then begun to draw the attention of the civilized world. Bonaparte had stained his laurels by the unprecedented baseness of his private conduct; he had not scrupled to turn Turk, and all his public proclamations were disgraced by the absurd phrases of Mohammedan superstition: Nelson, on the other hand, had no occasion of showing that he was an Englishman and a Christian: the first words of his despatches on this memorable occasion prove his gratitude to that Providence which had protected him: *"Almighty God has blessed his Majesty's arms."*

THE SOLDIER'S FUNERAL

IT is the funeral march. I did not think
   That there had been such magic in sweet sounds!
Hark! from the blackened cymbal that dead tone—
It awes the very rabble multitude.

THE SOLDIER'S FUNERAL

They follow silently, their earnest brows
Lifted in solemn thought. 'Tis not the pomp
And pageantry of death that with such force
Arrests the sense,— the mute and mourning train,
The white plume nodding o'er the sable hearse,
Had passed unheeded, or perchance awoke
A serious smile upon the poor man's cheek
At Pride's last triumph. Now these measured
    sounds,
This universal language, to the heart
Speak instant, and on all these various minds
Compel one feeling.

           But such better thoughts
Will pass away, how soon! and these who here
Are following their dead comrade to the grave,
Ere the night fall, will in their revelry
Quench all remembrance. From the ties of life
Unnaturally rent, a man who knew
No resting-place, nor no delights at home,
Belike who never saw his children's face,
Whose children knew no father, he is gone,
Dropp'd from existence, like the wither'd leaf
That from the summer tree is swept away,
Its loss unseen. She hears not of his death
Who bore him, and already for her son
Her tears of bitterness are shed; when first
He had put on the livery of blood,
She wept him dead to her.

           We are indeed
Clay in the potter's hand! one favor'd mind,
Scarce lower than the angels, shall explore
The ways of Nature, whilst his fellow-man,
Framed with like miracle the work of God,
Must as the unreasonable beast drag on
A life of labor, like this soldier here,
His wondrous faculties bestow'd in vain,
Be moulded to his fate till he becomes
A mere machine of murder.

61

                              And there are
Who say that this is well! as God has made
All things for man's good pleasure, so of men
The many for the few! court-moralists,
Reverend lip-comforters, that once a week
Proclaim how blessed are the poor, for they
Shall have their wealth hereafter, and though now
Toiling and troubled, though they pick the crumbs
That from the rich man's table fall, at length
In Abraham's bosom rest with Lazarus.
Themselves meantime secure their good things here
And feast with Dives. These are they, O Lord,
Who in thy plain and simple Gospel see
All mysteries, but who find no peace enjoin'd,
No brotherhood, no wrath denounced on them
Who shed their brethren's blood,—blind at noonday
As owls, lynx-eyed in darkness!
                              O my God!
I thank thee that I am not such as these;
I thank thee for the eye that sees, the heart
That feels, the voice that in these evil days,
Amid these evil tongues, exalts itself
And cries aloud against iniquity.

EDMUND C. STEDMAN

(Houghton, Mufflin & Co., Publishers)

EDMUND CLARENCE STEDMAN, "the banker poet" and critic, was born in Hartford, Conn., in 1833. He studied at Yale College, and then entered journalism. In 1864 he gave up journalism for a literary career. Until quite recently he was a member of the New York Stock Exchange, of which institution he has written the history. Among his books are: "Alice of Monmouth and other Poems," "The Blameless Prince," "A Victorian Anthology," "An American Anthology" and other works, criticisms, poems, etc.

PAN IN WALL STREET

JUST where the Treasury's marble front
  Looks over Wall Street's mingled nations;
Where Jews and Gentiles most are wont
  To throng for trade and last quotations;
Where, hour by hour, the rates of gold
  Outrival, in the ears of people,
The quarter-chimes, serenely tolled
  From Trinity's undaunted steeple,—

Even there I heard a strange, wild strain
  Sound high above the modern clamor,
Above the cries of greed and gain,
  The curbstone war, the auction's hammer;
And swift, on Music's misty ways,
  It led, from all this strife for millions,
To ancient, sweet-do-nothing days
  Among the kirtle-robed Sicilians.

And as it stilled the multitude,
  And yet more joyous rose, and shriller,
I saw the minstrel, where he stood
  At ease against a Doric pillar:
One hand a droning organ played,
  The other held a Pan's pipe (fashioned
Like those of old) to lips that made
  The reeds give out that strain impassioned.

'T was Pan himself had wandered here
  A-strolling through this sordid city,
And piping to the civic ear
  The prelude of some pastoral ditty!
The demigod had crossed the seas,—
  From haunts of shepherd, nymph, and satyr,
And Syracusan times,—to these
  Far shores and twenty centuries later.

A ragged cap was on his head;
  But—hidden thus—there was no doubting
That, all with crispy locks o'erspread,
  His gnarlèd horns were somewhere sprout-
    ing;
His club-feet, cased in rusty shoes,
  Were crossed, as on some frieze you see them,
And trousers, patched of divers hues,
  Concealed his crooked shanks beneath them.

He filled the quivering reeds with sound,
  And o'er his mouth their changes shifted,
And with his goat's eyes looked around
  Where'er the passing current drifted;
And soon, as on Trinacrian hills
  The nymphs and herdsmen ran to hear him,
Even now the tradesmen from their tills,
  With clerks and porters, crowded near him.

PAN IN WALL STREET

The bulls and bears together drew
  From Jauncey Court and New Street Alley,
As erst, if pastorals be true,
  Came beasts from every wooded valley;
The random passers stayed to list,—
  A boxer Ægon, rough and merry,
A Broadway Daphnis, on his tryst
  With Naïs at the Brooklyn Ferry.

A one-eyed Cyclops halted long
  In tattered cloak of army pattern;
And Galatea joined the throng,—
  A blowsy, apple-vending slattern;
While old Silenus staggered out
  From some new-fangled lunch-house handy,
And bade the piper, with a shout,
  To strike up Yankee Doodle Dandy!

A newsboy and a peanut girl
  Like little fauns began to caper:
His hair was all in tangled curl,
  Her tawny legs were bare and taper;
And still the gathering larger grew,
  And gave its pence and crowded nigher,
While aye the shepherd-minstrel blew
  His pipe, and struck the gamut higher.

O heart of Nature, beating still
  With throbs her vernal passion taught her,
Even here, as on the vine-clad hill,
  Or by the Arethusan water!
New forms may fold the speech, new lands
  Arise within these ocean-portals,
But Music waves eternal wands,—
  Enchantress of the souls of mortals!

So thought I,—but among us trod
  A man in blue, with legal baton,
And scoffed the vagrant demigod,
  And pushed him from the step I sat on.

Doubting I mused upon the cry,
    "Great Pan is dead!"—and all the people
Went on their ways;—and clear and high
    The quarter sounded from the steeple.

THE DIAMOND WEDDING

O LOVE! Love! Love! what times were those
    Long ere the age of belles and beaux,
And Brussels lace and silken hose,
When, in the green Arcadian close,
You married Psyche under the rose,
    With only the grass for bedding!
Heart to heart, and hand to hand,
You followed Nature's sweet command,
Roaming lovingly through the land,
    Nor sighed for a Diamond Wedding.

So have we read, in classic Ovid,
How Hero watched for her belovèd,
    Imprisoned youth, Leander,
She was the fairest of the fair,
And wrapt him round with her golden hair,
Whenever he landed cold and bare,
With nothing to eat and nothing to wear,
    And wetter than any gander;
For Love was Love, and better than money;
The slyer the theft, the sweeter the honey;
And kissing was clover, all the world over,
    Wherever Cupid might wander.
So thousands of years have come and gone,
And still the moon is shining on,
    Still Hymen's torch is lighted;
And hitherto, in this land of the West,
Most couples in love have thought it best
To follow the ancient way of the rest,
    And quietly get united.

THE DIAMOND WEDDING

But now, True Love, you're growing old—
Bought and sold, with silver and gold,
　Like a house, or a horse and carriage!
　　　Midnight talks,
　　　Moonlight walks,
The glance of the eye and sweetheart sigh,
The shadowy haunts, with no one by,
　I do not wish to disparage;
　　　But every kiss
　　　Has a price for its bliss,
In the modern code of marriage;
　　　And the compact sweet
　　　Is not complete
Till the high contracting parties meet
　Before the altar of Mammon;
And the bride must be led to a silver bower,
Where pearls and rubies fall in a shower
That would frighten Jupiter Ammon!

　　　I need not tell
　　　How it befell,
(Since Jenkins has told the story
Over and over and over again,
In a style I cannot hope to attain,
　And covered himself with glory!)
How it befell, one summer's day,
The king of the Cubans strolled this way—
King January's his name, they say—
And fell in love with the Princess May,
　The reigning belle of Manhattan;
For how he began to smirk and sue,
And dress as lovers who come to woo,
Or as Max Maretzek and Jullien do,
When they sit full-bloomed in the ladies' view,
　And flourish the wondrous baton.

He wasn't one of your Polish nobles,
Whose presence their country somehow troubles,

And so our cities receive them;
Nor one of your make-believe Spanish grandees,
Who ply our daughters with lies and candies,
    Until the poor girls believe them.
No, he was no such charlatan—
Count de Hoboken Flash-in-the-pan,
Full of gasconade and bravado—
But a regular, rich Don Rataplan,
Santa Claus de la Muscovado,
Señor Grandissimo Bastinado.
His was the rental of half Havana
And all Matanzas; and Santa Anna,
Rich as he was, could hardly hold
A candle to light the mines of gold
Our Cuban owned, choke-full of diggers;
And broad plantations, that, in round figures,
Were stocked with at least five thousand niggers!

"Gather ye rosebuds while ye may!"
The Señor swore to carry the day,
To capture the beautiful Princess May,
    With his battery of treasure;
Velvet and lace she should not lack;
Tiffany, Haughwout, Ball & Black,
Genin and Stewart his suit should back,
    And come and go at her pleasure;
Jet and lava—silver and gold—
Garnets—emeralds rare to behold—
Diamonds—sapphires—wealth untold—
All were hers, to have and to hold:
    Enough to fill a peck-measure!

He didn't bring all his forces on
At once, but like a crafty old Don,
Who many a heart had fought and won,
    Kept bidding a little higher;

And every time he made his bid,
And what she said, and all they did—
    'Twas written down,
      For the good of the town,
By Jeems, of *The Daily Flyer*.

A coach and horses, you'd think, would buy
For the Don an easy victory;
  But slowly our Princess yielded.
A diamond necklace caught her eye,
But a wreath of pearls first made her sigh.
She knew the worth of each maiden glance,
And, like young colts, that curvet and prance,
She led the Don a deuce of a dance,
    In spite of the wealth he wielded.

She stood such a fire of silks and laces,
Jewels and gold dressing-cases,
And ruby brooches, and jets and pearls,
That every one of her dainty curls
Brought the price of a hundred common girls;
  Folks thought the lass demented!
But at last a wonderful diamond ring,
An infant Koh-i-noor, did the thing,
And, sighing with love, or something the same,
    (What's in a name?)
The Princess May consented.

Ring! ring the bells, and bring
The people to see the marrying!
Let the gaunt and hungry and ragged poor
Throng round the great cathedral door,
To wonder what all the hubbub's for,
  And sometimes stupidly wonder
At so much sunshine and brightness, which
Fall from the church upon the rich,
  While the poor get all the thunder.

Ring, ring! merry bells, ring!
O fortunate few,
With letters blue,
Good for a seat and a nearer view!
Fortunate few, whom I dare not name;
Dilettanti! Crême de la crême!

We commoners stood by the street façade,
And caught a glimpse of the cavalcade.
We saw the bride
In diamonded pride,
With jeweled maidens to guard her side—
Six lustrous maidens in tarletan.
She led the van of the caravan;
Close behind her, her mother
(Dressed in gorgeous *moire antique,*
That told, as plainly as words could speak,
She was more antique than the other)
Leaned on the arm of Don Rataplan
Santa Claus de la Muscovado,
Señor Grandissimo Bastinado.
Happy mortal! fortunate man!
And Marquis of El Dorado!

In they swept, all riches and grace,
Silks and satins, jewels and lace;
In they swept from the dazzled sun,
And soon in the church the deed was done.
Three prelates stood on the chancel high:
A knot that gold and silver can buy,
Gold and silver may yet untie,
Unless it is tightly fastened;
What's worth doing at all's worth doing well,
And the sale of a young Manhattan belle
Is not to be pushed or hastened;
So two Very-Reverends graced the scene,
And the tall Archbishop stood between,
By prayer and fasting chastened.

THE DIAMOND WEDDING

The Pope himself would have come from Rome,
But Garibaldi kept him at home.
Haply these robed prelates thought
Their words were the power that tied the knot;
But another power that love-knot tied,
And I saw the chain round the neck of the bride—
A glistening, priceless, marvelous chain,
Coiled with diamonds again and again,
　As befits a diamond wedding;
Yet still 'twas a chain, and I thought she knew it,
And halfway longed for the will to undo it,
　By the secret tears she was shedding.

But isn't it odd to think, whenever
We all go through that terrible River—
Whose sluggish tide alone can sever
(The Archbishop says) the Church decree,
By floating one into Eternity
And leaving the other alive as ever—
As each wades through that ghastly stream,
The satins that rustle and gems that gleam,
Will grow pale and heavy, and sink away
To the noisome River's bottom-clay!
Then the costly bride and her maidens six
Will shiver upon the bank of the Styx,
Quite as helpless as they were born—
Naked souls, and very forlorn;
The Princess, then must shift for herself,
And lay her royalty on the shelf;
She, and the beautiful Empress, yonder,
Whose robes are now the wide world's wonder,
And even ourselves, and our dear little wives,
Who calico wear each morn of their lives,
And the sewing-girls, and *les chiffonniers,*
In rags and hunger—a gaunt array—
And all the grooms of the caravan—
Ay, even the great Don Rataplan

71

Santa Claus de la Muscovado
Señor Grandissimo Bastinado—
That gold-encrusted, fortunate man—
All will land in naked equality:
The lord of a ribboned principality
 Will mourn the loss of his *cordon;*
Nothing to eat and nothing to wear
Will certainly be the fashion there!
Ten to one, and I'll go it alone;
Those most used to a rag and bone,
Though here on earth they labor and groan,
Will stand it best, as they wade abreast
 To the other side of Jordan.
1859.

THE DOOR-STEP

THE conference-meeting through at last,
 We boys around the vestry waited
To see the girls come tripping past,
 Like snow-birds willing to be mated.

Not braver he that leaps the wall
 By level musket-flashes litten,
Than I, who stepped before them all
 Who longed to see me get the mitten.

But no: she blushed and took my arm!
 We let the old folks have the highway,
And started toward the Maple Farm
 Along a kind of lover's by-way.

I can't remember what we said—
 'Twas nothing worth a song or story;
Yet that rude path by which we sped
 Seemed all transformed, and in a glory.

The snow was crisp beneath our feet,
  The moon was full, the fields were gleaming;
By hood and tippet sheltered sweet,
  Her face with youth and health was beaming.

The little hand outside her muff—
  O sculptor, if you could but mould it!
So lightly touched my jacket-cuff
  To keep it warm I had to hold it.

To have her with me there alone,
  'Twas love and fear and triumph blended,
At last we reached the foot-worn stone
  Where that delicious journey ended.

The old folks, too, were almost home;
  Her dimpled hand the latches fingered;
We heard the voices nearer come,
  Yet on the door-step still we lingered.

She shook her ringlets from her hood
  And with a " Thank you, Ned," dissembled;
But yet I knew she understood
  With what a daring wish I trembled.

A cloud passed kindly overhead,
  The moon was slyly peeping through it,
Yet hid its face, as if it said—
  " Come, now or never! do it! *do it.*"

My lips till then had only known
  The kiss of mother and of sister;
But somehow, full upon her own
  Sweet, rosy, darling mouth—I kissed her!

Perhaps 'twas boyish love, yet still—
  O listless woman, weary lover!—
To feel once more that fresh, wild thrill
  I'd give—but who can live youth over?

LAURENCE STERNE

LAURENCE STERNE, clergyman and novelist, born of English parents in Clonmel, Ireland, in 1713; died in London in 1768. He was educated at Oxford University, England, took orders in the church, and became rector of Sutton-in-the-Forest, Yorkshire. Later he was transferred to York Cathedral. In 1759 he published the first two volumes of "The Life and Opinions of Tristram Shandy," the last appearing in 1767. His fame rests on the above, together with "The Sentimental Journey through France and Italy."

THE DEAD ASS

(From "A Sentimental Journey")

AND this," said he, putting the remains of a crust into his wallet,—"and this should have been thy portion," said he, "hadst thou been alive to have shared it with me." I thought, by the accent, it had been an apostrophe to his child; but 'twas to his ass, and to the very ass we had seen dead in the road, which had occasioned La Fleur's misadventure. The man seemed to lament it much: and it instantly brought into my mind Sancho's lamentations for his; but he did it with more true touches of nature.

The mourner was sitting upon a stone bench at the door, with the ass's pannel and its bridle on one side, which he took up from time to time—then laid them down—looked at them, and shook his head. He then took his crust of bread out of his wallet again, as if to eat it; held it some time in his

hand; then laid it upon a bit of his ass's bridle,
looked wistfully at the little arrangement he had
made, and then gave a sigh.

The simplicity of his grief drew numbers about
him, and La Fleur amongst the rest, whilst the
horses were getting ready: as I continued sitting
in the post-chaise, I could see and hear over their
heads.

He said he had come last from Spain, where he
had been from the furtherest borders of Franconia;
and had got so far on his return home, when his
ass died. Every one seemed desirous to know what
business could have taken so old and poor a man so
far a journey from his own home.

It had pleased Heaven, he said, to bless him with
three sons, the finest lads in all Germany; but having in one week lost two of the eldest of them by
the smallpox, and the youngest falling ill of the
same distemper, he was afraid of being bereft of
them all; and made a vow, if Heaven would not
take him from him also, he would go in gratitude
to St. Iago in Spain.

When the mourner got thus far on his story, he
stopped to pay nature his tribute, and wept bitterly.

He said Heaven had accepted the conditions; and
that he had set out from his cottage with this poor
creature, which had been a patient partner of his
journey; that it had ate the same bread with him
all the way, and was unto him as a friend.

Everybody who stood about heard the poor fellow
with concern. La Fleur offered him money. The
mourner said he did not want it: it was not the
value of the ass, but the loss of him. The ass, he
said, he was assured, loved him: and upon this, told
them a long story of a mischance upon their passage over the Pyrenean mountains, which had separated them from each other three days; during which
time the ass had sought him as much as he had

sought the ass, and that they had scarce either ate or drank till they met.

"Thou hast one comfort, friend," said I, "at least, in the loss of thy poor beast: I'm sure thou hast been a merciful master to him!" "Alas!" said the mourner, "I thought so when he was alive: but now that he is dead, I think otherwise; I fear that the weight of myself and my afflictions together have been too much for him—they have shortened the poor creature's days, and I fear I have them to answer for." "Shame on the world!" said I to myself. "Did we but love each other as this poor soul loved his ass—'twould be something."

THE STARLING

(From "A Sentimental Journey")

I WAS interrupted in the heyday of this soliloquy with a voice which I took to be that of a child, which complained it could not get out. I looked up and down the passage, and seeing neither man, woman, nor child, I went out without further attention.

In my return back through the passage, I heard the same words repeated twice over, and looking up, I saw it was a starling hung in a little cage. "I can't get out! I can't get out!" said the starling.

I stood looking at the bird; and to every person who came through the passage it ran fluttering to the side toward which they approached it, with the same lamentation of its captivity. "I can't get out!" said the starling.

"God help thee!" said I, "but I'll help thee out, cost what it will;" so I turned about the cage to get to the door;—it was twisted and double twisted so fast with wire, there was no getting it open without pulling the cage to pieces. I took both hands to it.

The bird flew to the place where I was attempting his deliverance, and thrusting his head through the trellis, pressed his breast against it as if impatient.

"I fear, poor creature," said I, "I cannot set thee at liberty."

"No," said the starling: "I can't get out! I can't get out!" said the starling.

I vow I never had my affections more tenderly awakened; nor do I remember an incident in my life where the dissipated spirits, to which my reason had been a bubble, were so suddenly called home. Mechanical as the notes were, yet so true in tune to nature were they chanted, that in one moment they overthrew all my systematic reasonings upon the Bastile; and I heavily walked upstairs, unsaying every word I had said in going down them.

"Disguise thyself as thou wilt, still, Slavery," said I,—"still thou art a bitter draught! and though thousands in all ages have been made to drink thee, thou art no less bitter on that account. 'Tis thou, thrice sweet and gracious goddess," addressing myself to Liberty, "whom all in public or in private worship; whose taste is grateful, and ever will be so, till Nature herself shall change. No tint of words can spot thy snowy mantle, or chemic power turn thy sceptre into iron; with thee to smile upon him as he eats his crust, the swain is happier than his monarch from whose court thou art exiled. "Gracious Heaven!" cried I, kneeling down upon the last step but one in my ascent, "grant me but health, thou great Bestower of it, and give me but this fair goddess as my companion; and shower down thy mitres, if it seems good unto thy Divine providence, upon those heads which are aching for them."

The bird in his cage pursued me into my room. I sat down close to my table, and leaning my head upon my hand, I began to figure to myself the miseries of confinement. I was in a right frame for it, and so I gave full scope to my imagination.

I was going to begin with the millions of my fellow-creatures born to no inheritance but slavery; but finding, however affecting the picture was, that I could not bring it near me, and that the multitudes of sad groups in it did but distract me—I took a single captive, and having first shut him up in his dungeon, I then looked through the twilight of his grated door to take his picture.

I beheld his body half wasted away with long expectation and confinement, and felt what kind of sickness of heart it is which arises from hope deferred. Upon looking nearer, I saw him pale and feverish: in thirty years, the western breeze had not once fanned his blood; he had seen no sun, no moon, in all that time, nor had the voice of friend or kinsman breathed through his lattice! his children——

But here my heart began to bleed, and I was forced to go on with another part of the portrait.

He was sitting upon the ground, upon a little straw in the furtherest corner of his dungeon, which was alternately his chair and bed: a little calendar of small sticks was laid at his head, notched all over with the dismal days and nights he had passed there; he had one of those little sticks in his hand, and with a rusty nail he was etching another day of misery to add to the heap.

As I darkened the little light he had, he lifted up a hopeless eye toward the door; then cast it down, shook his head, and went on with his work of affliction. I heard his chains upon his legs, as he turned his body to lay his little stick upon the bundle. He gave a deep sigh—I saw the iron enter into his soul!

I burst into tears.—I could not sustain the picture of confinement which my fancy had drawn. I started up from my chair, and calling La Fleur, I

id him bespeak me a *remise,* and have it ready at
ie door of the hotel by nine in the morning.

" I'll go directly," said I to myself, " to Monsieur
: Duc le Choiseul."

La Fleur would have put me to bed; but not will-
ig he should see anything upon my cheek which
ould cause the honest fellow a heartache, I told
im I would go to bed myself, and bid him do the
ame.

I got into my *remise* the hour I proposed; La
'leur got up behind, and I bid the coachman make
he best of his way to Versailles.

As there was nothing in this road, or rather noth-
ig which I look for in traveling, I cannot fill up
he blank better than with a short history of this
elfsame bird, which became the subject of the last
hapter.

Whilst the Honorable Mr. —— was waiting for a
rind at Dover, it had been caught upon the cliffs,
efore it could well fly, by an English lad who was
is groom: who not caring to destroy it, had taken
t in his breast into the packet; and by course of
eeding it, and taking it once under his protection,
1 a day or two grew fond of it, and got it safe
long with him to Paris.

At Paris, the lad had lain out a livre in a little
age for the starling; and as he had little to do
etter, the five months his master stayed there, he
aught it in his mother's tongue the four simple
vords (and no more) to which I owed myself so
nuch its debtor.

Upon his master's going on for Italy the lad had
;iven it to the master of the hotel.

But this little song for liberty being in an un-
:nown language at Paris the bird had little or no
tore set by him; so La Fleur bought him and his
age for me for a bottle of burgundy.

In my return from Italy, I brought him with me

to the country in whose language he had learned
his notes; and telling the story of him to Lord A
Lord A begged the bird of me; in a week Lord A
gave him to Lord B; Lord B made a present of him
to Lord C; and Lord C's gentleman sold him to
Lord D's for a shilling; Lord D gave him to Lord
E; and so on—half round the alphabet. From that
rank he passed into the lower house, and passed the
hands of as many commoners. But as all these
wanted to get in, and my bird wanted to get out, he
had almost as little store set by him in London as
at Paris.

It is impossible but many of my readers must
have heard of him; and if any by mere chance have
ever seen him, I beg leave to inform them that that
bird was my bird, or some vile copy set up to
represent him.

It have nothing farther to add upon him, but that
from that time to this I have borne this poor starling as the crest to my arms:—And let the herald's
officers twist his neck about if they dare.

ROBERT LOUIS STEVENSON

(Charles Scribner's Sons, Publishers)

ROBERT LOUIS STEVENSON, Scotch novelist, poet and essayist, was born in Edinburgh in 1850; died in Apia, Samoa, in 1894. He belonged to a family of famous engineers; prepared for the bar, but took up literary work. First he contributed short articles and stories to magazines, and then began to write the books that gave him an enviable place among British writers. Among his best are: "Treasure Island," "The Strange Case of Dr. Jekyll and Mr. Hyde," "Kidnapped," "The Black Arrow," "David Balfour" and "The Master of Ballantrae. The originality of his plots, freshness of his style and correct English have been seldom surpassed.

MY SHORE ADVENTURE

(From "Treasure Island")

THE appearance of the island when I came on deck next morning was altogether changed. Although the breeze had now utterly failed, we had made a great deal of way during the night, and were now lying becalmed about half a mile to the south-east of the low eastern coast. Gray-colored woods covered a large part of the surface. This even tint was indeed broken up by streaks of yellow sand-break in the lower lands, and by many tall trees of the pine family, out-topping the others— some singly, some in clumps; but the general coloring was uniform and sad. The hills ran up clear above the vegetation in spires of naked rock. All were strangely shaped, and the Spy-glass, which was by three or four hundred feet the tallest on the island, was likewise the strangest in configuration, running up sheer from almost every side, and then suddenly cut off at the top like a pedestal to put a statue on.

The "Hispaniola" was rolling scuppers under in the ocean swell. The booms were tearing at the blocks, the rudder was banging to and fro, and the whole ship creaking, groaning, and jumping like a manufactory. I had to cling tight to the backstay, and the world turned giddily before my eyes; for though I was a good enough sailor when there was way on, this standing still and being rolled about like a bottle was a thing I never learned to stand without a qualm or so, above all in the morning, on an empty stomach.

Perhaps it was this—perhaps it was the look of the island, with its gray, melancholy woods, and wild stone spires, and the surf that we could both see and hear foaming and thundering on the steep beach—at least, although the sun shone bright and hot, and the shore birds were fishing and crying all around us, and you would have thought any one would have been glad to get to land after being so long at sea, my heart sunk, as the saying is, into my boots; and from that first look onward, I hated the very thought of Treasure Island.

We had a dreary morning's work before us, for there was no sign of any wind, and the boats had to be got out and manned, and the ship warped three or four miles round the corner of the island, and up the narrow passage to the haven behind Skeleton Island. I volunteered for one of the boats, where I had, of course, no business. The heat was sweltering, and the men grumbled fiercely over their work. Anderson was in command of my boat, and instead of keeping the crew in order, he grumbled as loud as the worst.

"Well," he said, with an oath, "it's not forever."

I thought this was a very bad sign; for, up to that day, the men had gone briskly and willingly about their business; but the very sight of the island had relaxed the cords of discipline.

All the way in, Long John stood by the steersman and conned the ship. He knew the passage like the palm of his hand; and though the man in the chains got everywhere more water than was down in the chart, John never hesitated once.

"There's a strong scour with the ebb," he said, "and this here passage has been dug out, in a manner of speaking, with a spade."

We brought up just where the anchor was in the chart, about a third of a mile from either shore, the mainland on one side, and Skeleton Island on the other. The bottom was clean sand. The plunge of our anchor sent up clouds of birds wheeling and crying over the woods; but in less than a minute they were all down again, and all was once more silent.

The place was entirely land-locked, buried in woods, the trees coming right down to high water mark, the shores mostly flat, and the hill-tops standing round at a distance in a sort of amphitheater, one here, one there. Two little rivers, or, rather, two swamps, emptied out into this pond, as you might call it; and the foliage round that part of the shore had a kind of poisonous brightness. From the ship, we could see nothing of the house or stockade, for they were quite buried among trees; and if it had not been for the chart on the companion, we might have been the first that had ever anchored there since the island arose out of the seas.

There was not a breath of air moving, nor a sound but that of the surf booming half a mile away along the beaches and against the rocks outside. A peculiar stagnant smell hung over the anchorage—a smell of sodden leaves and rotten tree trunks. I observed the doctor sniffing and sniffing, like some one tasting a bad egg.

"I don't know about treasure," he said, "but I'll stake my wig there's fever here."

If the conduct of the men had been alarming in the boat, it became truly threatening when they had come aboard. They lay about the deck growling together in talk. The slightest order was received with a black look, and grudgingly and carelessly obeyed. Even the honest hands must have caught the infection, for there was not one man aboard to mend another. Mutiny, it was plain, hung over us like a thunder-cloud.

And it was not only we of the cabin party who perceived the danger. Long John was hard at work going from group to group, spending himself in good advice, and as for example no man could have shown a better. He fairly outstripped himself in willingness and civility; he was all smiles to every one. If an order were given, John would be on his crutch in an instant, with the cheeriest "Ay, ay, sir!" in the world; and when there was nothing else to do, he kept up one song after another, as if to conceal the discontent of the rest.

Of all the gloomy features of that gloomy afternoon, this obvious anxiety on the part of Long John appeared the worst.

We held a council in the cabin.

"Sir," said the captain, "if I risk another order, the whole ship'll come about our ears by the run. You see, sir, here it is. I get a rough answer, do I not? Well, if I speak back, pikes will be going in two shakes; if I don't, Silver will see there's something under that, and the game's up. Now, we've only one man to rely on."

"And who is that?" asked the squire.

"Silver, sir," returned the captain; "he's as anxious as you and I to smother things up. This is a tiff; he'd soon talk 'em out of it if he had the chance, and what I propose to do is to give him the chance. Let's allow the men an afternoon ashore. If they all go, why, we'll fight the ship. If they none of them go, well, then, we hold the cabin, and God defend the right. If some go, you mark my words, sir, Silver'll bring 'em aboard again as mild as lambs."

It was so decided; loaded pistols were served out to all the sure men; Hunter, Joyce, and Redruth were taken into our confidence, and received the news with less surprise and a better spirit than we had looked for, and then the captain went on deck and addressed the crew.

"My lads," said he, "we've had a hot day, and are all tired and out of sorts. A turn ashore'll hurt nobody—the boats are still in the water; you can take the gigs, and as many as please can go ashore for the afternoon. I'll fire a gun half an hour before sun-down."

I believe the silly fellows must have thought they would break their shins over the treasure as soon as they were landed; for they all came out of their sulks in a moment, and gave a cheer that started the echo in a far-away hill, and sent the birds once more flying and squalling round the anchorage.

The captain was too bright to be in the way. He whipped out of sight in a moment, leaving Silver to arrange the party; and I fancy it was as well he did so. Had he been on deck, he could no longer so much as have pretended not to understand the situation. It was as plain as day. Silver was the captain, and a mighty rebellious crew he had of it. The honest hands—and I was soon to see it proved that there were such on board—must have been very stupid fellows. Or, rather, I suppose the truth was this: that all hands were disaffected by the example of the ringleaders—only some more, some less; and a few, being good fellows in the main, could neither be led nor driven any further. It is one thing to be idle and skulk, and quite another to take a ship and murder a number of innocent men.

At last, however, the party was made up. Six fellows were to stay on board, and the remaining thirteen, including Silver, began to embark.

Then it was that there came into my head the first of the mad notions that contributed so much to save our lives. If six men were left by Silver, it was plain our party could not take and fight the ship; and since only six were left, it was equally plain that the cabin party had no present need of my assistance. It occurred to me at once to go ashore. In a jiffy I had slipped over the side, and curled up in the fore-sheets of the nearest boat, and almost at the same moment she shoved off.

No one took notice of me, only the bow oar saying, "Is that you, Jim? Keep your head down." But Silver, from the other boat, looked sharply over and called out to know if that were me; and from that moment I began to regret what I had done.

The crews raced for the beach; but the boat I was in, having some start, and being at once the lighter and the better manned, shot far ahead of her consort, and the bow had struck among the shore-side trees, and I had caught a branch and swung myself out, and plunged into the nearest thicket, while Silver and the rest were still a hundred yards behind.

"Jim, Jim!" I heard him shouting.

But you may suppose I paid no heed; jumping, ducking, and breaking through, I ran straight before my nose, till I could run no longer.

THE HOUSE OF SHAWS

(From "Kidnapped")

ON the forenoon of the second day, coming to the top of a hill, I saw all the country fall away before me down to the sea; and in the midst of this descent, on a long ridge, the city of Edinburgh smoking like a kiln. There was a flag upon the castle, and ships moving or lying anchored in the firth, both of which, for as far away as they were, I could distinguish clearly; and both brought my country heart into my mouth.

Presently after, I came by a house where a shepherd lived, and got a rough direction for the neighborhood of Cramond; and so, from one to another, worked my way to the westward of the capital by Colinton, till I came out upon the Glasgow road. And there, to my great pleasure and wonder, I beheld a regiment marching to the fifes, every foot in time; an old red-faced general on a gray horse at the one end, and at the other the company of Grenadiers, with their Pope's-hats. The pride of life seemed to mount into my brain at the sight of the red-coats and the hearing of that merry music.

A little farther on, and I was told I was in Cramond parish, and began to substitute in my inquiries the name of the house of Shaws. It was a word that seemed to surprise those of whom I sought my way. At first I thought the plainness of my appearance, in my country habit, and that all lusty from the road, consorted ill with the greatness of the place to which I was bound. But after two, or maybe three, had given me the same look and the same answer, I began to take it in my head there was something strange about the Shaws itself.

87

The better to set this fear at rest, I changed the form of my inquiries; and spying an honest fellow coming along a lane on the shaft of his cart, I asked him if he had ever heard tell of a house they called the house of Shaws.

He stopped his cart and looked at me, like the others.

"Ay," said he. "What for?"

"It's a great house?" I asked.

"Doubtless," says he. "The house is a big, muckle house."

"Ay," said I, "but the folk that are in it?"

"Folk?" cries he. "Are ye daft? There's nae folk there—to call folk."

"What?" says I; "not Mr. Ebenezer?"

"O, ay," says the man; "there's the laird, to be sure, if it's him you're wanting. What'll like be your business, mannie?"

"I was led to think that I would get a situation," I said, looking as modest as I could.

"What?" cries the carter, in so sharp a note that his very horse started; and then, "Well, mannie," he added, "it's name of my affairs; but ye seem a decent-spoken lad; and if ye'll take a word from me, ye'll keep clear of the Shaws."

The next person I came across was a dapper little man in a beautiful white wig, whom I saw to be a barber on his rounds: and knowing well that barbers were great gossips, I asked him plainly what sort of a man was Mr. Balfour of the Shaws.

"Hoot, hoot, hoot," said the barber, "nae kind of a man, nae kind of a man at all;" and began to ask me very shrewdly what my business was; but I was more than a match for him at that, and he went on to his next customer no wiser than he came.

I cannot well describe the blow this dealt to my illusions. The more indistinct the accusations were, the less I liked them, for they left the wider field to fancy. What kind of a great house was this, that all the parish should start and stare to be asked the way to it? or what sort of a gentleman, that his ill-fame should be thus current on the wayside? If an hour's walking would have brought me back to Essendean, I had left my adventure then and there, and returned to Mr. Campbell's. But when I had come so far away already, mere shame would not suffer me to desist till I had put the matter to the touch of proof; I was bound, out of mere self-respect, to carry it through; and little as I liked the sound of what I heard, and slow as I began to travel, I still kept asking my way and still kept advancing.

It was drawing on to sundown when I met a stout, dark, sour-looking woman coming trudging down a hill; and she, when I had put my usual question, turned sharp about, accompanied me back to the summit she had just left, and pointed to a great bulk of building standing very bare upon a green in the bottom of the next valley. The country was pleasant round about, running low hills, pleasantly watered and wooded, and the crops, to my eyes, wonderfully good; but the house itself appeared to be a kind of ruin; no road led up to it; no smoke arose from any of the chimneys; nor was there any semblance of a garden. My heart sank. "That!" I cried.

The woman's face lit up with a malignant anger. "That is the house of Shaws!" she cried. "Blood built it; blood stopped the building of it; blood shall bring it down. See here!" she cried again—"I spit upon the ground, and crack my thumb at it! Black be its fall! If ye see the laird, tell him what ye hear; tell him this makes the twelve hunner and nineteen time that Jennet Clouston has called down the curse on him and his house, byre and stable, man, guest, and master, wife, miss, or bairn—black, black be their fall!"

And the woman, whose voice had risen to a kind of eldritch sing-song, turned with a skip, and was gone. I stood where she left me, with my hair on end. In these days folks still believe in witches and trembled at a curse; and this one, falling so pat, like a wayside omen, to arrest me ere I carried out my purpose, took the pith out of my legs.

I sat me down and stared at the house of Shaws. The more I looked, the pleasanter that country-side appeared; being all set with hawthorn bushes full of flowers; the fields dotted with sheep; a fine flight of rooks in the sky; and every sign of a kind soil and climate; and yet the barrack in the midst of it went sore against my fancy.

Country folk went by from the fields as I sat there on the side of the ditch, but I lacked the spirit to give them a good-e'en. At last the sun went down, and then, right up against the yellow sky, I saw a scroll of smoke go mounting, not much thicker, as it seemed to me, than the smoke of a candle; but still there it was, and meant a fire, and warmth, and cookery, and some living inhabitant that must have lit it; and this comforted my heart wonderfully—more, I feel sure, than a whole flask of the lily of the valley water that Mrs. Campbell set so great a store by.

So I set forward by a little faint track in the grass that led in my direction. It was very faint indeed to be the only way to a place of habitation; yet I saw no other. Presently it brought me to stone uprights, with an unroofed lodge beside them, and coats of arms upon the top. A main entrance, it was plainly meant to be, but never finished; instead of gates of wrought iron, a pair of hurdles were tied across with a straw rope; and as there were no park walls, nor any sign of avenue, the track that I was following passed on the right hand of the pillars, and went wandering on toward the house.

The nearer I got to that, the drearier it appeared. It seemed like the one wing of a house that had never been finished. What should have been the inner end stood open on the upper floors, and showed against the sky with steps and stairs of uncompleted masonry. Many of the windows were unglazed, and bats flew in and out like doves out of a dove-cote.

The night had begun to fall as I got close; and in three of the lower windows, which were very high up, and narrow, and well barred, the changing light of a little fire began to glimmer.

Was this the palace I had been coming to? Was it within these walls that I was to seek new friends and begin great fortunes? Why, in my father's house on Essen-Waterside, the fire and the bright lights would show a mile away, and the door open to a beggar's knock.

I came forward cautiously, and giving ear as I came, heard some one rattling with dishes, and a little dry, eager cough that came in fits; but there was no sound of speech, and not a dog barked.

The door, as well as I could see it in the dim light, was a great piece of wood all studded with nails; and I lifted my hand with a faint heart under my jacket, and knocked once. Then I stood and waited. The house had fallen into a dead silence; a whole minute passed away, and nothing stirred but the bats overhead. I knocked again, and hearkened again. By this time my ears had grown so accustomed to the quiet, that I could hear the ticking of the clock inside as it slowly counted out the seconds; but whoever was in that house kept deadly still, and must have held his breath.

I was in two minds whether to run away; but anger got the upper hand, and I began instead to rain kicks and buffets on the door, and to shout out aloud for Mr. Balfour. I was in full career, when I heard the cough right overhead, and jumping back and looking up, beheld a man's head in a tall night-cap, and the bell mouth of a blunderbuss, at one of the first story windows.

"It's loaded," said a voice.

"I have come here with a letter," I said, "to Mr. Ebenezer Balfour of Shaws. Is he here?"

"From whom is it?" asked the man with the blunderbuss.

"That is neither here nor there," said I, for I was growing very wroth.

"Well," was the reply, "ye can put it down upon the doorstep, and be off with ye."

"I will do no such a thing," I cried. "I will deliver it into Mr. Balfour's hands, as it was meant I should. It is a letter of introduction."

"A what?" cried the voice, sharply.

I repeated what I had said.

"Who are ye, yourself?" was the next question, after a considerable pause.

"I am not ashamed of my name," said I. "They call me David Balfour."

At that, I made sure the man started, for I heard the blunderbuss rattle on the window-sill; and it was after quite a long pause, and with a curious change of voice, that the next question followed:

"Is your father dead?"

I was so much surprised at this, that I could find no voice to answer, but stood staring.

"Ay," the man resumed, "he'll be dead, no doubt; and that'll be what brings ye chapping to my door." Another pause, and then, defiantly, "Well, man," he said, "I'll let ye in;" and he disappeared from the window.

THE LOSS OF THE BRIG

(From "Kidnapped")

IT was already late at night, and as dark as it ever would be at that season of the year (and that is to say, it was still pretty bright), when Hoseason clapped his head into the round-house door.

"Here," said he, "come out and see if ye can pilot."

"Is this one of your tricks?" asked Alan.

"Do I look like tricks?" cries the captain. "I have other things to think of—my brig's in danger!"

By the concerned look of his face, and, above all, by the sharp tones in which he spoke of his brig, it was plain to both of us he was in deadly earnest; and so Alan and I, with no great fear of treachery, stepped on deck.

The sky was clear; it blew hard, and was bitter cold; a great deal of daylight lingered; and the moon, which was nearly full, shone brightly. The brig was close hauled, so as to round the southwest corner of the Island of Mull; the hills of which (and Ben More above them all, with a wisp of mist upon the top of it) lay full upon the larboard bow. Though it was no good point of sailing for the *Covenant,* she tore through the seas at a great rate, pitching and straining, and pursued by the westerly swell.

Altogether it was no such ill night to keep the seas in; and I had begun to wonder what it was that sat so heavily upon the captain, when the brig rising suddenly on the top of a high swell he pointed and cried to us to look. Away on the lee bow, a thing like a fountain rose out of the moonlit sea, and immediately after we heard a low sound of roaring.

"What do ye call that?" asked the captain gloomily.

93

"The sea breaking on a reef," said Alan. "And now ye ken where it is; and what better would ye have?"

"Ay," said Hoseason, "if it was the only one."

And sure enough just as he spoke there came a second fountain further to the south.

"There!" said Hoseason. "Ye see for yourself. If I had kent of these reefs, if I had had a chart, or if Shuan had been spared, it's not sixty guineas, no, nor six hundred, would have made me risk my brig in sic a stoneyard! But you, sir, that was to pilot us, have ye never a word?"

"I'm thinking," said Alan, "these'll be what they call the Torran Rocks."

"Are there many of them?" says the captain.

"Truly, sir, I am nae pilot," said Alan; "but it sticks in my mind there are ten miles of them."

Mr. Riach and the captain looked at each other.

"There's a way through them, I suppose?" said the captain.

"Doubtless," said Alan; "but where? But it somehow runs in my mind once more, that it is clearer under the land."

"So?" said Hoseason. "We'll have to haul our wind then, Riach; we'll have to come as near in about the end of Mull as we can take her, sir; and even then we'll have the land to keep the wind off us, and that stoneyard on our lee. Well, we're in for it now, and may as well crack on."

With that he gave an order to the steersman, and sent Riach to the foretop. There were only five men on deck, counting the officers; these were all that were fit (or, at least, both fit and willing) for their work; and two of these were hurt. So, as I say, it fell to Mr. Riach to go aloft, and he sat there looking out and hailing the deck with news of all he saw.

"The sea to the south is thick," he cried; and

then, after awhile, "It does seem clearer in by the land."

"Well, sir," said Hoseason to Alan, "we'll try your way of it. But I think I might as well trust to a blind fiddler. Pray God you're right."

"Pray God I am!" says Alan to me. "But where did I hear it? Well, well, it will be as it must."

As we got nearer to the turn of the land the reefs began to be sown here and there on our very path; and Mr. Riach sometimes cried down to us to change the course. Sometimes, indeed, none too soon; for one reef was so close on the brig's weather board that when a sea burst upon it the lighter sprays fell upon her deck and wetted us like rain.

The brightness of the night showed us these perils as clearly as by day, which was, perhaps, the more alarming. It showed me, too, the face of the captain as he stood by the steersman, now on one foot, now on the other, and sometimes blowing in his hands, but still listening and looking and as steady as steel. Neither he nor Mr. Riach had shown well in the fighting; but I saw they were brave in their own trade, and admired them all the more because I found Alan very white.

"Ochone, David," said he, "this is no the kind of death I fancy."

"What, Alan!" I cried, "you're not afraid?"

"No," said he, wetting his lips, "but you'll allow yourself, it's a cold ending."

By this time, now and then sheering to one side or the other to avoid a reef, but still hugging the wind and the land, we had got round Iona and begun to come alongside Mull. The tide of the tail of the land ran very strong, and threw the brig about. Two hands were put to the helm, and Hoseason himself would sometimes lend a help;

and it was strange to see three strong men throw their weight upon the tiller, and it (like a living thing) struggle against and drive them back. This would have been the greater danger, had not the sea been for some while free of obstacles. Mr. Riach, besides, announced from the top that he saw clear water ahead.

"Ye were right," said Hoseason to Alan. "Ye have saved the brig, sir; I'll mind that when we come to clear accounts." And I believe he not only meant what he said, but would have done it; so high a place did the *Covenant* hold in his affections.

But this is matter only for conjecture, things having gone otherwise than he forecast.

"Keep her away a point," sings out Mr. Riach. "Reef to windward!"

And just at the same time the tide caught the brig, and threw the wind out of her sails. She came round into the wind like a top, and the next moment struck the reef with such a dunch as threw us all flat upon the deck, and came near to shake Mr. Riach from his place upon the mast.

I was on my feet in a minute. The reef on which we had struck was close in under the southwest end of Mull, off a little isle they call Earraid, which lay low and black upon the larboard. Sometimes the swell broke clean over us; sometimes it only ground the poor brig upon the reef, so that we could hear her beat herself to pieces; and what with the great noise of the sails, and the singing of the wind, and the flying of the spray in the moonlight, and the sense of danger, I think my head was partly turned, for I could scarcely understand the things I saw.

Presently, I observed Mr. Riach and the seamen busy round the skiff; and still in the same blank, ran over to assist them; and as soon as I set my hand to work, my mind came clear again. It was no very easy task, for the skiff lay amidships and was full of hamper, and the breaking of the heavier seas continually forced us to give over and hold on; but we all wrought like horses while we could.

Meanwhile such of the wounded as could move came clambering out of the forescuttle and began to help; whiel the rest that lay helpless in their bunks harrowed me with screaming and begging to be saved.

The captain took no part. It seemed he was struck stupid. He stood holding by the shrouds, talking to himself and groaning out aloud whenever the ship hammered on the rock. His brig was like wife and child to him; he had looked on, day by day, at the mishandling of poor Raasome; but when it came to the brig, he seemed to suffer along with her.

All the time of our working at the boat, I remember only one other thing: that I asked Alan, looking across at the shore, what country it was; and he answered, it was the worst possible for him, for it was a land of the Campbells.

We had one of the wounded men told off to keep a watch upon the seas and cry us warning. Well, we had the boat about ready to be launched, when this man sang out pretty shrill: "For God's sake, hold on!" We knew by his tone that it was something more than ordinary; and sure enough, there followed a sea so huge that it lifted the brig right up and canted her over on her beam. Whether the cry came too late or my hold was too weak, I know not; but at the sudden tilting of the ship, I was cast clean over the bulwarks into the sea.

I went down, and drank my fill; and then came up, and got a blink of the moon; and then down again. They say a man sinks the third time for good. I cannot be made like other folk, then, for I would not like to write how often I went down or how often I came up again. All the while, I was being hurled along, and beaten upon and choked, and then swallowed whole; and the thing was so distracting to my wits, that I was neither sorry nor afraid.

Presently, I found I was holding to a spar, which helped me somewhat. And then all of a sudden I was in quiet water, and began to come to myself.

It was the spare yard I had got hold of, and I was amazed to see how far I had traveled from the brig. I hailed her, indeed; but it was plain she was already out of cry. She was still holding together; but whether or not they had yet launched the boat, I was too far off and too low down to see.

While I was hailing the brig, I spied a tract of water lying between us, where no great waves came but which yet boiled white all over and bristled in the moon with rings and bubbles. Sometimes the whole tract swung to one side, like the tail of a live serpent; sometimes, for a glimpse, it all would disappear and then boil up again. What it was I had no guess, which for the time increased my fear of it; but I now know it must have been the roost of tide-race, which had carried me away so fast and tumbled me about so cruelly, and at last, as if tired of that play, had flung out me and the spare yard upon its landward margin.

I now lay quite becalmed, and began to feel that a man can die of cold as well as of drowning. The shores of Earraid were close in; I could see in the moonlight the dots of heather and the sparkling of the mica in the rocks.

"Well," thought I to myself, "if I cannot get as far as that, it's strange."

I had no skill of swimming, Essen water being small in our neighborhood; but when I laid hold upon the yard with both arms, and kicked out with both feet, I soon began to find that I was moving

Hard work it was, and mortally slow; but in about an hour of kicking and splashing, I had got well in between the points of a sandy bay surrounded by low hills.

The sea was here quite quiet; there was no sound of any surf; the moon shone clear; and I thought in my heart I had never seen a place so desert and desolate. But it was dry land; and when at last it grew so shallow that I could leave the yard and wade ashore upon my feet, I cannot tell if I was more tired or more grateful. Both at least, I was: tired as I never was before that night; and grateful to God, as I trust I have been often, though never with more cause.

RICHARD H. STODDARD

(Charles Scribner's Sons, Publishers)

RICHARD HENRY STODDARD, an American poet, was born in Hingham, Mass., in 1825. He died in New York in 1903. His first volume, entitled "Foot-prints," appeared in 1849. He has been a frequent contributor to the leading American newspapers and magazines. Among his best works are: "Melodies and Madrigals from old English Poets," "The Book of the East," "The King's Bell" and "Songs of Summer." His critical writing on English and American literature will always hold a high place with students and lovers of the best in literary art.

WIND AND RAIN

R ATTLE the window, Winds!
    Rain, drip on the panes!
There are tears and sighs in our hearts and eyes
    And a weary weight on our brains.

The gray sea heaves and heaves,
    On the dreary flats of sand;
And the blasted limb of the churchyard yew,
    It shakes like a ghostly hand!

The dead are engulfed beneath it,
    Sunk in the grassy waves;
But we have more dead in our hearts to-day
    Than the Earth in all her graves!

THE COUNTRY LIFE

NOT what we would, but what we must,
    Makes up the sum of living;
Heaven is both more and less than just
    In taking and in giving.
Swords cleave to hands that sought the plough,
And laurels miss the soldier's brow.

Me, whom the city holds, whose feet
    Have worn its stony highways,
Familiar with its loneliest street—
    Its ways were never my ways.
My cradle was beside the sea,
And there, I hope, my grave will be.

Old homestead! In that old, gray town,
    Thy vane is seaward blowing,
The slip of garden stretches down
    To where the tide is flowing:
Below they lie, their sails all furled,
The ships that go about the world.

Dearer that little country house,
    Inland, with pines beside it;
Some peach-trees, with unfruitful boughs,
    A well, with weeds to hide it:
No flowers, or only such as rise
Self-sown, poor things, which all despise.

Dear country home! Can I forget
    The least of thy sweet trifles?
The window-vines that clamber yet,
    Whose bloom the bee still rifles?
The roadside blackberries, growing ripe,
And in the woods the Indian Pipe?

Happy the man who tills his field,
  Content with rustic labor;
Earth does to him her fulness yield,
  Hap what may to his neighbor.
Well days, sound nights, oh, can there be
A life more rational and free?

Dear country life of child and man!
  For both the best, the strongest,
That with the earliest race began,
  And hast outlived the longest:
Their cities perished long ago;
Who the first farmers were we know.

Perhaps our Babels too will fall;
  If so, no lamentations,
For Mother Earth will shelter all,
  And feed the unborn nations;
Yes, and the swords that menace now
Will then be beaten to the plough.

THE FLIGHT OF YOUTH

THERE are gains for all our losses.
    There are balms for all our pain:
But when youth, the dream, departs
It takes something from our hearts,
    And it never comes again.

We are stronger, and are better,
    Under manhood's sterner reign:
Still we feel that something sweet
Followed youth, with flying feet,
    And will never come again.

THE FLIGHT OF YOUTH

Something beautiful is vanished,
  And we sigh for it in vain;
We behold it everywhere,
On the earth, and in the air,
  But it never comes again!

HARRIET BEECHER STOWE

HARRIET BEECHER STOWE, novelist, born in Litch-
field, Conn., in 1812; died in Hartford, Conn., in
1896. She belonged to the celebrated Beecher
family. In 1826 she married Professor Calvin E.
Stowe. She wrote much and with marked public
acceptance. Among her books are: "My Wife and
I," "The Minister's Wooing" and "Old Town
Folks." The last will ever be read for its
quaint humor and graphic delineation of character.
Her fame rests, however, on the story, "Uncle Tom's
Cabin," which so powerfuully advocated the aboli-
tion of slavery. It gave a vivid picture of social
conditions now passed into history. It has been
translated into nearly all written languages.

THE PARSON'S HORSE-RACE

(From "Old Town Folks")

WAL, now, this 'ere does beat all!   I wouldn't
'a' thought it o' the deacon."
So spoke Sam Lawson, drooping in a discouraged,
contemplative attitude in front of an equally discouraged looking horse, that had just been brought
to him by the Widow Simpkins for medical treat-
ment. Among Sam's many accomplishments, he was
reckoned in the neighborhood an oracle in all
matters of this kind, especially by women, whose
helplessness in meeting such emergencies found unfailing solace under his compassionate willingness
to attend to any business that did not strictly belong to him, and from which no pecuniary return
was to be expected.
The Widow Simpkins had bought this horse of
Deacon Atkins, apparently a fairly well-appointed

brute, and capable as he was good-looking. A short, easy drive, when the Deacon held the reins, had shown off his points to advantage; and the widow's small stock of ready savings had come forth freely in payment for what she thought was a bargain. When, soon after coming into possession, she discovered that her horse, if driven with any haste, panted in a fearful manner, and that he appeared to be growing lame, she waxed wroth, and went to the Deacon in anger, to be met only with the smooth reminder that the animal was all right when she took him; that she had seen him tried herself. The widow was of a nature somewhat spicy, and expressed herself warmly: "It's a cheat and a shame, and I'll take the law on ye!"

"What law will you take?" said the unmoved Deacon. "Wasn't it a fair bargain?"

"I'll take the law of God," said the widow, with impotent indignation; and she departed to pour her cares and trials into the ever-ready ear of Sam. Having assumed the care of the animal, he now sat contemplating it in a sort of trance of melancholy reflection.

"Why, boys," he broke out, "why didn't she come to me afore she bought this crittur? Why, I knew all about him! That 'ere crittur was jest ruined a year ago last summer, when Tom, the Deacon's boy there, come home from college. Tom driv him over the Sherburn and back that 'ere hot Fourth of July. 'Member it, 'cause I saw the crittur when he come home. I sot up with Tom takin' care of him all night. That 'ere crittur had the thumps all night, and he hain't never been good for nothin' since. I telled the Deacon he was a gone hoss then, and wouldn't never be good for nothin'. The Deacon, he took off his shoes, and let him run to pastur' all summer, and he's ben a-feedin' and nussin' on him up; and now he's put him off on the widder. I wouldn't 'a' thought it o' the Deacon! Why, this hoss'll never be no good to her! That 'ere's a used-up crittur, any fool may see! He'll mabbe do for about a quarter of an hour on a smooth road; but come to drive him as a body wants to drive, why, he blows like my bellowsis; and the Deacon knew it—must 'a' known it!"

"Why, Sam!" we exclaimed, "ain't the Deacon a good man?"

"Wal, now, there's where the shoe pinches! In a gin'al way the Deacon *is* a good man—he's considable more than middlin' good; gin'ally he adorns his perfession. On most p'ints I don't hev nothin' agin the Deacon; and this 'ere ain't a bit like him. But there 'tis! Come to hosses, there's where the unsanctified natur' comes out. Folks will cheat about hosses when they won't about 'most nothin' else." And Sam leaned back on his cold forge, now empty of coal, and seemed to deliver himself to a mournful train of general reflection. "Yes, hosses does seem to be sort o' unregenerate critturs," he broke out: "there's suthin about hosses that deceives the very elect. The best o' folks gets tripped up when they come to deal in hosses."

"Why, Sam, is there anything bad in horses?" we interjected timidly.

"'Tain't the hosses," said Sam with solemnity. "Lordy massy! the hosses is all right enough! Hosses is scriptural animals. Elijah went up to heaven in a chari't with hosses, and then all them lots o' hosses in the Ravelations—black and white and red, and all sorts o' colors. That 'ere shows hosses goes to heaven; but it's more'n the folks that hev 'em is likely to, ef they don't look out.

"Ministers, now," continued Sam, in a soliloquizing vein—"folks allers thinks it's suthin' sort o' shaky in a minister to hev much to do with hosses—sure to get 'em into trouble. There was old Parson

Williams of North Billriky got into a drefful mess about a hoss. Lordy massy! he wern't to blame, neither; but he got into the dreffulest scrape you ever heard on—come nigh to unsettlin' him."

"O Sam, tell us all about it!" we boys shouted, delighted with the prospect of a story.

"Wal, wait now till I get off this crittur's shoes, and we'll take him up to pastur', and then we can kind o' set by the river, and fish. Hepsy wanted a mess o' fish for supper, and I was cal'latin' to git some for her. You boys go and be digging bait, and git yer lines."

And so, as we were sitting tranquilly beside the Charles River, watching our lines, Sam's narrative began:

"Ye see, boys, Parson Williams—he's dead now, but when I was a boy he was one of the gret men round here. He writ books. He writ a tract agin the Armenians, and put 'em down; and he writ a big book on the millennium (I've got that 'ere book now); and he was a smart preacher. Folks said he had invitations to settle in Boston, and there ain't no doubt he might 'a' hed a Boston parish ef he'd 'a' ben a mind ter take it; but he'd got a good settlement and a handsome farm in North Billriky, and didn't care to move; thought, I s'pose, that 'twas better to be number one in a little place than number two in a big un. Anyway, he carried all before him where he was.

"Parson Williams was a tall, straight, personable man; come of good family—father and grand'ther before him all ministers. He was putty up and down, and commandin' in his ways, and things had to go putty much as he said. He was a good deal sot by, Parson Williams was, and his wife was a Derby—one o' them rich Salem Derbys—and brought him a lot o' money; and so they lived putty easy and comfortable so fur as this world's goods goes.

Well, now, the parson wa'n't reely what you call worldly-minded; but then he was one o' them folks that *knows what's good* in temporals as well as sperituals, and allers liked to hev the best that there was goin'; and he allers had an eye to a good hoss.

"Now, there was Parson Adams and Parson Scranton, and most of the other ministers: they didn't know and didn't care what hoss they hed; jest jogged round with these 'ere poundin', potbellied, sleepy critturs that ministers mostly hes— good enough to crawl around to funerals and ministers' meetin's and 'sociations and sich; but Parson Williams, he allers would hev a hoss as was a hoss. He looked out for *blood;* and, when these 'ere Vermont fellers would come down with a drove, the parson he hed his eyes open, and knew what was what. Couldn't none of 'em cheat him on hoss flesh! And so one time when Zach Buel was down with a drove, the doctor he bought the best hoss in the lot. Zach said he never see a parson afore that he couldn't cheat; but he said the doctor reely knew as much as he did, and got the very one he'd meant to 'a' kept for himself.

"This 'ere hoss was a peeler, I'll tell you! They'd called him Tamerlane, from some heathen feller or other: the boys called him Tam, for short. Tam was a great character. All the fellers for miles round knew the doctor's Tam, and used to come clear over from the other parishes to see him.

"Wal, this 'ere sot up Cuff's back high, I tell you. Cuff was the doctor's nigger man, and he was nat'lly a drefful proud crittur. The way he would swell and strut and brag about the doctor and his folks and his things! The doctor used to give Cuff his cast-off clothes: and Cuff would prance round in 'em, and seen to think he was a doctor of divinity himself, and had the charge of all natur'.

"Well, Cuff he reely made an idol o' that 'ere

hoss—a reg'lar graven image—and bowed down and worshiped him. He didn't think nothin' was too good for him. He washed and brushed and curried him, and rubbed him down till he shone like a lady's satin dress; and he took pride in ridin' and drivin' him, cause it was what the doctor wouldn't let nobody else do but himself. You see, Tam wern't no lady's hoss. Miss Williams was 'fraid as death of him; and the parson he hed to git her a sort o' low-sperited crittur that she could drive herself. But he liked to drive Tam; and he liked to go round the country on his back, and a fine figure of a man he was on him, too. He didn't let nobody else back him or handle the reins but Cuff; and Cuff was dreful set up about it, and he swelled and bragged about that ar hoss all round the country. Nobody couldn't put in a word 'bout any other hoss, without Cuff's feathers would be all up stiff as a tom-turkey's tail; and that's how Cuff got the doctor into trouble.

"Ye see, there nat'lly was others that thought they'd got horses, and didn't want to be crowed over. There was Bill Atkins, out to the west parish, and Ike Sanders, that kep' a stable up to Pequot Holler: they was down a-lookin' at the parson's hoss, and a-bettin' on their'n, and a darin' Cuff to race with 'em.

"Wal, Cuff, he couldn't stan' it, and, when the doctor's back was turned, he'd be off on the sly, and they'd hev their race; and Tam he beat 'em all. Tam, ye see, boys, was a hoss that couldn't and wouldn't hev a hoss ahead of him—he jest *wouldn't!* Ef he dropped down dead in his tracks the next minit, he *would* be ahead; and he allers got ahead. And so his name got up, and fellers kep' comin' to try their horses: and Cuff'd take Tam out to race with fust one and then another till this 'ere got to be a reg'lar thing, and begun to be talked about.

"Folks sort o' wondered if the doctor knew; but Cuff was sly as a weasel, and allers had a story ready for every turn. Cuff was one of them fellers that could talk a bird off a bush—master hand he was to slick things over!

"There was folks as said they believed the doctor was knowin' to it, and that he felt a sort o' carnal pride sech as a minister oughtn't fer to hev, and so shet his eyes to what was a-goin' on. Aunt Sally Nickerson said she was sure on't. 'Twas all taked over down to old Miss Bummiger's funeral, and Aunt Sally she said the church ought to look into't. But everybody knew Aunt Sally: she was allers watchin' for folks' haltin's, and settin' on herself up to jedge her neighbors.

"Wal, I never believed nothin' agin Parson Williams: it was all Cuff's contrivances. But the fact was, the fellers all got their blood up, and there was hoss-racin' in all the parishes; and it got so they'd race hosses a Sunday.

"Wal, of course they never got the doctor's hoss out a Sunday. Cuff wouldn't 'a' dust do that, Lordy massy, no! He was allers there in church, settin' up in the doctor's clothes, rollin' up his eyes, and lookin' as pious as ef he never thought o' racin' hosses. He was an awful solemn-lookin' nigger in church, Cuff was.

"But there was a lot o' them fellers up to Pequot Holler—Bill Atkins, and Ike Sanders, and Tom Peters, and them Hokum boys—used to go out arter meetin' Sunday afternoon, and race hosses. Ye see, it was jest close to the State-line, and, if the s'lectmen was to come down on 'em, they could jest whip over the line, and they couldn't take 'em.

"Wal, it got to be a great scandal. The fellers talked about it up to the tavern; and the deacons and the tithingman, they took it up and went to Parson Williams about it; and the parson he told

'em jest to keep still, not let the fellers know that
they was bein' watched, and next Sunday he and the
tithingman and the constable, they'd ride over, and
catch 'em in the very act.

"So next Sunday arternoon Parson Williams and
Deacon Popkins and Ben Bradley (he was constable
that year), they got on to their hosses, and rode over
to Pequot Holler. The doctor's blood was up, and
he mean to come down on 'em strong; for that was
his way o' doin' in his parish. And they was in a
sort o' day-o'-jedgment frame o' mind, and jogged
along solemn as a hearse, till, come to rise the hill
above the holler, they see three or four fellers with
their hosses gittin' ready to race; and the parson
says he, 'Let's come on quiet, and get behind these
bushes, and we'll see what they're up to, and catch
'em in the act.'

"But the michief on't was, that Ike Sanders see
'em comin,' and he knowed Tam in a minit—Ike
knowed Tam of old—and he jest tipped the wink to
the rest. 'Wait, boys,' says he: 'let 'em git close
up, and then I'll give the word, and the doctor's hoss'
will be racin' like thunder.'

"Wal, so the doctor and his folks they drew up
behind the bushes, and stood there innocent as could
be, and saw 'em gittin' ready to start. Tam, he
begun to snuffle and paw, but the doctor never mis-
trusted what he as up to till Ike sung out, 'Go it,
boys!' and the hosses all started, when, sure as you
live, boys! Tam give one fly, and was over the
bushes, and in among 'em, goin' it like chain-light-
nin' ahead of 'em all.

"Deacon Popkins and Ben Bradley jest stood and
held their breath to see 'em all goin' it so like thunder; and the doctor, he was took so sudden it was
all he could do to jest hold on anyway: so away
he went, and trees and bushes and fences streaked
by him like ribbins. His hat flew off behind him,

and his wig arter, and got catched in a barberry-
bush; but Lord massy! he couldn't stop to think o'
them. He jest leaned down, and caught Tam round
the neck, and held on for dear life till they come to
the stopping-place.

"Wal, Tam was ahead of them all, sure enough,
and was snorting and snuffling as if he'd got the
very old boy in him, and was up to racing some
more on the spot.

"That 'ere Ike Sanders was the impudentest feller
that ever you see, and he roared and rawhawed at
the doctor. 'Good for you, parson!' says he. 'You
beat us all holler!" says he. 'Takes a parson for
that, don't it, boys?' he said. And then he and Ike
and Tom, and the two Hokum boys, they jest roared,
and danced round like wild critturs. Wal, now, only
think on't, boys, what a situation that 'ere was for
a minister—a man that had come out with the best
of motives to put a stop to Sabbath-breakin'! There
he was all rumpled up and dusty, and his wig hang-
in' in the bushes, and these 'ere ungodly fellers get-
tin' the laugh on him, and all acause o' that 'ere hoss.
There's times, boys, when ministers must be tempted
to swear, if there ain't preventin' grace, and this was
one o' them times to Parson Williams. They say he
got red in the face, and looked as if he should bust,
but he didn't say nothin': he scorned to answer. The
sons o' Zeruiah was too hard for him, and he let 'em
hev their say. But when they'd got through, and
Ben had brought him his hat and wig, and brushed
and settled him ag'in, the parson he says, "Well,
boys, ye've had your say and your laugh; but I
warn you now I won't have this thing goin' on here
any more,' says he; 'so mind yourselves.'

"Wal, the boys see that the doctor's blood was
up, and they rode off pretty quiet; and I believe
they never raced no more in that spot.

"But there ain't no tellin' the talk this 'ere thing

made. Folks will talk, you know; and there wer'n't a house in all Billriky, nor in the south parish nor center, where it wer'n't had over and discussed. There was the deacon, and Ben Bradley was there, to witness and show jest how the thing was, and that the doctor was jest in the way of his duty; but folks said it made a great scandal; that a minister hadn't no business to hev that kind o' hoss, and that he'd give the enemy occasion to speak reproachfully. It reely did seem as if Tam's sins was imputed to the doctor; and folks said he ought to sell Tam right away, and get a sober minister's hoss.

"But others said it was Cuff that had got Tam into bad ways; and they do say that Cuff had to catch it pretty lively when the doctor come to settle with him. Cuff thought his time had come, sure enough, and was so scairt that he turned blacker'n ever: he got enough to cure him o' hoss-racin' for one while. But Cuff got over it arter a while, and so did the doctor. Lord massy! there ain't nothin' lasts forever! Wait long enough, and 'most everything blows over. So it turned out about the doctor. There was a rumpus and a fuss, and folks talked and talked, and advised; everybody had their say: but the doctor kep' right straight on, and kep' his hoss all the same.

"The ministers, they took it up in the 'sociation; but, come to tell the story, it sot 'em all a-laughin', so they couldn't be very hard on the doctor.

"The doctor felt sort o' streaked at fust when they told the story on him; he didn't jest like it: but he got used to it, and finally, when he was twitted on't, he'd sort o' smile, and say, 'Anyway, Tam beat 'em: that's one comfort.'"

TOPSY

(From " Uncle Tom's Cabin ")

ONE morning, while Miss Ophelia was busy in some of her domestic cares, St. Clare's voice was heard, calling he at the foot of the stairs.

" Come down here, cousin; I've something to show you."

"What is it?" said Miss Opehlia, coming down, with her sewing in her hand.

" I've made a purchase for your department—see here," said St. Clare; and, with the word, he pulled along a little negro girl, about eight or nine years of age.

She was one of the blackest of her race; and her round, shining eyes, glittering as glass beads, moved with quick and restless glances over everything in the room. Her mouth, half open with astonishment at the wonders of the new Mas'r's parlor, displayed a white and brilliant set of teeth. Her woolly hair was braided in sundry little tails, which stuck out in every direction. The expression of her face was an odd mixture of shrewdness and cunning, over which was oddly drawn, like a kind of veil, an expression of the most doleful gravity and solemnity. She was dressed in a single filthy, ragged garment, made of bagging; and stood with her hands demurely folded before her. Altogether, there was something odd and goblin-like about her appearance, —something, as Miss Ophelia afterwards said, " so heathenish," as to inspire that good lady with utter dismay; and, turning to St. Clare, she said:

" Augustine, what in the world have you brought that thing here for?"

"For you to educate, to be sure, and train in the way she should go. I thought she was rather a funny specimen in the Jim Crow line. Here, Topsy," he added, giving a whistle, as a man would call the attention of a dog, "gives us a song, now, and show us some of your dancing."

The black, glassy eyes glittered with a kind of wicked drollery, and the thing struck up, in a clear shrill voice, an old negro melody, to which she kept time with her hands and feet, spinning round, clapping her hands, knocking her knees together, in a wild, fantastic sort of time, and producing in her throat all those odd guttural sounds which distinguish the native music of her race; and finally, turning a somerset or two, and giving a prolonged closing note, as odd and unearthly as that of a steam-whistle, she came suddenly down on the carpet, and stood with her hands folded, and a most sanctimonious expression of meekness and solemnity over her face, only broken by the cunning glances which she shot askance from the corners of her eyes.

Miss Ophelia stood silent, perfectly paralyzed with amazement.

St. Clare, like a mischievous fellow as he was, appeared to enjoy her astonishment; and, addressing the child again, said:

"Topsy, this is your new mistress. I'm going to give you up to her; see, now, that you behave yourself."

"Yes, Mas'r," said Topsy, with sanctimonious gravity, her wicked eyes twinkling as she spoke.

"You're going to be good, Topsy, you understand," said St. Clare.

"Oh, yes, Mas'r," said Topsy, with another twinkle, her hands still devoutly folded.

"Now, Augustine, what upon earth is this for?" said Miss Ophelia. "Your house is so full of these little plagues, now, that a body can't set down their foot without treading on 'em. I get up in the morning, and find one asleep behind the door, and see one black head poking out from under the table, one

115

lying on the door-mat,—and they are mopping and mowing and grinning between all the railings, and tumbling over the kitchen floor! What on earth did you want to bring this one for?"

"For you to educate,—didn't I tell you? You're always preaching about educating. I thought I would make you a present of a fresh-caught specimen, and let you try your hand on her, and bring her up in the way she should go."

"*I* don't want her, I am sure;—I have more to do with 'em now than I want to."

"That's you Christians, all over!—you'll get up a society, and get some poor missionary to spend all his days among just such heathen. But let me see one of you that would take one into your house with you, and take the labor of their conversion on yourselves! No; when it comes to that, they are dirty and disagreeable, and it's too much care, and so on."

"Augustine, you know I didn't think of it in that light," said Miss Ophelia, evidently softening. "Well, it might be a real missionary work," said she, looking rather more favorably on the child.

St. Clare had touched the right string. Miss Ophelia's conscientiousness was ever on the alert. "But," she added, "I really didn't see the need of buying this one;—there are enough now, in your house, to take all my time and skill."

"Well, then, cousin," said St. Clare, drawing her aside, "I ought to beg your pardon for my good-for-nothing speeches. You are so good, after all, that there's no sense in them. Why, the fact is, this concern belonged to a couple of drunken creatures that keep a low restaurant that I have to pass by every day, and I was tired of hearing her screaming, and them beating and swearing at her. She looked bright and funny, too, as if something might be made of her,—so I bought her, and I'll give her to you.

Try, now, and give her a good orthodox New England bringing up, and see what it'll make of her. You know I haven't any gift that way; but I'd like you to try."

"Well, I'll do what I can," said Miss Ophelia; and she approached her new subject very much as a person might be supposed to approach a black spider, supposing them to have benevolent designs toward it.

"She's dreadfully dirty, and half naked," she said.

"Well, take her down stairs, and make some of them clean and clothe her up."

Miss Ophelia carried her to the kitchen regions.

"Don't see what Mas'r St. Clare wants of 'nother nigger!" said Dinah, surveying the new arrival with no friendly air. "Won't have her round under *my* feet, *I* know!"

"Pah!" said Rosa and Jane, with supreme disgust; "let her keep out of our way! What in the world Mas'r wanted another of these low niggers for, I can't see!"

"You go 'long! No more nigger dan you be, Miss Rosa," said Dinah, who felt this last remark a reflection on herself. "You seem to tink yourself white folks. You an't nerry one, black *nor* white. I'd like to be one or turrer."

Miss Ophelia saw that there was nobody in the camp that would undertake to oversee the cleansing and dressing of the new arrival; and so she was forced to do it herself, with some very ungracious and reluctant assistance from Jane.

When she saw, on the back and shoulders of the child, great welts and calloused spots, ineffaceable marks of the system under which she had grown up thus far, her heart became pitiful within her.

"See there!" said Jane, pointing to the marks, "don't that show she's a limb? We'll have fine works with her, I reckon. I hate these nigger young

117

uns! so disgusting! I wonder that Mas'r would buy her!"

The "young un" alluded to heard all these comments with the subdued and doleful air which seemed habitual to her, only scanning, with a keen and furtive glance of her flickering eyes, the ornaments which Jane wore in her ears. When arrayed at last in a suit of decent and whole clothing, her hair cropped short to her head, Miss Ophelia, with some satisfaction, said she looked more Christian-like than she did, and in her own mind began to mature some plans for her instruction.

Sitting down before her, she began to question her.

"How old are you, Topsy?"

"Dunno, Missis," said the image, with a grin that showed all her teeth.

"Don't know how old you are? Didn't anybody ever tell you? Who was your mother?"

"Never had none!" said the child, with another grin.

"Never had any mother? What do you mean? Where were you born?"

"Never was born!" persisted Topsy, with another grin, that looked so goblin-like, that, if Miss Ophelia had been at all nervous, she might have fancied that she had got hold of some sooty gnome from the land of Diablerie; but Miss Ophelia was not nervous, but plain and business-like, and she said, with some sternness:

"You mustn't answer me in that way, child; I'm not playing with you. Tell me where you were born, and who your father and mother were."

"Never was born," reiterated the creature, more emphatically; "never had no father nor mother, nor nothin'. I was raised by a speculator, with lots of others. Old Aunt Sue used to take car on us."

The child was evidently sincere; and Jane, breaking into a short laugh, said:

"Laws, Missis, there's heaps of 'em. Speculators buys 'em up cheap, when they's little, and get's 'em raised for market."

"How long have you lived with your master and mistress?"

"Dunno, Missis."

"Is it a year, or more, or less?"

"Dunno, Missis."

"Laws, Missis, those low negroes,—they can't tell; they don't know anything about time," said Jane; "they don't know what a year is; they don't know their own ages."

"Have you ever heard anything about God, Topsy?"

The child looked bewildered, but grinned as usual.

"Do you know who made you?"

"Nobody, as I knows on," said the child, with a short laugh.

The idea appeared to amuse her considerably; for her eyes twinkled, and she added:

"I spect I grow'd. Don't think nobody never made me."

"Do you know how to sew?" said Miss Ophelia, who thought she would turn her inquiries to something more tangible.

"No, Missis."

"What can you do?—what did you do for your master and mistress?"

"Fetch water, and wash dishes, and rub knives, and wait on folks."

"Were they good to you?"

"Spect they was," said the child, scanning Miss Ophelia cunningly.

Miss Ophelia rose from this encouraging colloquy; St. Claire was leaning over the back of her chair.

"You find virgin soil there, cousin; put in your own ideas,—you won't find many to pull up."

SIR JOHN SUCKLING

SIR JOHN SUCKLING, dramatist and poet, was born in Whitton, Middlesex, in 1609; died in Paris, in 1642. He was educated at Cambridge University, and traveled extensively. As a soldier he distinguished himself under the great Gustavus Adolphus, of Sweden. He wrote many short plays and poems.

DESCRIPTION OF A BEAUTY

(From "A Ballad Upon a Wedding")

THE maid (and thereby hangs a tale)
  For such a maid no Whitson-ale
    Could ever yet produce:
No grape that's kindly ripe could be
So round, so plump, so soft as she,
    Nor half so full of juice.

Her feet beneath her petticoat,
Like little mice, stole in and out,
    As if they fear'd the light:
But, oh! she dances such a way!
No sun upon the Easter-day
    Is half so fine a sight.

Her cheeks so rare a white was on,
No daisy makes comparison
    (Who sees them is undone);
For streaks of red were mingled there,
Such as are on a Cath'rine pear,
    (The side that's next the sun.)

Her lips were red; and one was thin,
Compared to that was next her chin—
    Some bee had stung it newly.
But (Dick) her eyes so guard her face,
I durst no more upon them gaze
    Than on the sun in July.

Her mouth so small, when she does speak,
Thou'dst swear her teeth her words did break,
    That they might passage get;
But she so handled still the matter,
They came as good as ours, or better,
    And are not spent a whit.

THE FAINT-HEARTED LOVER

WHY so pale and wan, fond lover?
    Prithee why so pale?
Will, when looking well can't move her,
    Looking ill prevail?
    Prithee why so pale?

Why so dull and mute, young sinner?
    Prithee why so mute?
Will, when speaking well can't win her,
    Saying nothing do't?
    Prithee why so mute?

Quit, quit, for shame; this will not move,
    This cannot take her;
If of herself she will not love,
    Nothing can make her:
    The devil take her.

TO AN HONEST LOVER

HONEST lover whatsoever,
　If in all thy love there ever
Was one wavering thought; if thy flame
Were not still even, still the same:
　　　Know this,
　　　Thou lov'st amiss,
　　　And to love true,
Thou must begin again and love anew.

If when she appears i' th' room,
Thou dost not quake, and are struck dumb,
And in striving this to cover,
Dost not speak thy words twice over,
　　　Know this,
　　　Thou lov'st amiss,
　　　And to love true,
Thou must begin again and love anew.

If fondly thou dost not mistake,
And all defects for graces take,
Persuad'st thyself that jests are broken,
When she hath little or nothing spoken,
　　　Know this,
　　　Thou lov'st amiss,
　　　And to love true,
Thou must begin again and love anew.

If by this thou dost discover
That thou art no perfect lover,
And desiring to love true,
Thou dost begin to love anew,
　　　Know this,
　　　Thou lov'st amiss,
　　　And to love true,
Thou must begin again and love anew.

CONSTANCY

OUT upon it. I have loved
    Three whole days together;
And am like to love three more,
    If it prove fair weather.

Time shalt moult away his wings,
    Ere he shall discover
In the whole wide world again
    Such a constant lover.

But the spite on 't is, no praise
    Is due at all to me;
Love with me had made no stays,
    Had it any been but she.

Had it any been but she,
    And that very face,
There had been at least ere this
    A dozen in her place.

JONATHAN SWIFT

JONATHAN SWIFT, clergyman and humorist, was born of English parents in Dublin, Ireland, in 1667; died there in 1745. He was educated for the church, and after the death of Sir William Temple, to whom he had been secretary, he became Dean of St. Patrick's in Dublin. He was a victim of melancholia and went from the liveliest mood to deep despondency. His satire, "A Tale of a Tub," made him famous at once, and his later works shared its popularity. His "Battle of the Books" is still of interest, especially to scholars, and his famous "Gulliver's Travels" has amused the readers of nearly two centuries.

THE EMPEROR OF LILLIPUT

(From "The Voyage to Lilliput")

THE Emperor is taller by almost the breadth of my nail than any of his court, which alone is sufficient to strike an awe into the beholders. His features are strong and masculine, with an Austrian lip, and arched nose; his complexion olive, his countenance erect, his body and limbs well-proportioned, all his movements graceful, and his deportment majestic. He was then past his prime, being twenty-eight years and three-quarters old, of which he had reigned seven in great felicity, and generally victorious. For the better convenience of beholding him, I lay on my side, so that my face was parallel to his, and he stood but three yards off. However, I have had him since many times in my hand, and therefore cannot be mistaken in my description. His dress was very plain and simple, and the fashion of it between the Asiatic and the European; but he had on his head a light helmet of gold, adorned with jewels, and a plume on the crest. He held his sword drawn in his hand, to defend himself if I should happen to break loose. It was almost three inches long; the hilt and scabbard were gold, enriched with diamonds. His voice was shrill, but very clear and articulate; and I could distinctly hear it when I stood up. His Imperial Majesty spoke often to me, and I returned answers; but neither of us could understand a syllable.

THOUGHTS AND APHORISMS

AN old miser kept a tame jackdaw, that used to steal pieces of money, and hide them in a hole, which the cat observing, asked, " Why he would hoard up those round shining things that he could make no use of?"

"Why," said the jackdaw, "my master has a whole chestful, and makes no more use of them than I."

If the men of wit and genius would resolve never to complain in their works of critics and detractors, the next age would not know that they ever had any.

I never wonder to see men wicked, but I often wonder to see them not ashamed.

Imaginary evils soon become real ones, by indulging our reflections on them; as he, who in a melancholy fancy sees something like a face on the wall or the wainscot, can, by two or three touches with a lead pencil, make it look visible, and agreeing with what he fancied.

Men of great parts are often unfortunate in the management of public business, because they are apt to go out of the common road by the quickness of their imagination. This I once said to my Lord Bolingbroke, and desired he would observe, that the clerks in his office used a sort of ivory knife with a blunt edge to divide a sheet of paper, which never failed to cut it even, only requiring a steady hand; whereas if they should make use of a sharp penknife, the sharpness would make it often go out of the crease, and disfigure the paper.

"He who does not provide for his own house," St. Paul says, "is worse than an infidel." And I think he who provides only for his own house is just equal with an infidel.

When I am reading a book, whether wise or silly, it seems to me to be alive, and talking to me.

I never yet knew a wag (as the term is) who was not a dunce.

A person reading to me a dull poem of his own making, I prevailed on him to scratch out six lines together; in turning over the leaf, the ink being wet, it marked as many lines on the other side; whereof the poet complaining, I bid him be easy, for it would be better if those were out too.

We have just enough religion to make us hate, but not enough to make us love one another.

When we desire or solicit anything, our minds run wholly on the good side or circumstances of it; when it is obtained, our minds run wholly on the bad ones.

The latter part of a wise man's life is taken up in curing the follies, prejudices, and false opinions he had contracted in the former.

Would a writer know how to behave himself with relation to posterity, let him consider in old books what he finds that he is glad to know, and what omissions he most laments.

It is grown a word of course for writers to say, "this critical age," as divines say, "this sinful age."

It is pleasant to observe how free the present age is in laying taxes on the next: "Future ages shall talk of this: this shall be famous to all posterity;" whereas their time and thoughts will be taken up about present things, as ours are now.

I never heard a finer piece of satire against lawyers, than that of astrologers, when they pretend by rules of art to tell when a suit will end, and whether to the advantage of the plaintiff or defendant; thus making the matter depend entirely upon the influence of the stars, without the least regard to the merits of the cause.

I have known some men possessed of good qualities, which were very serviceable to others, but useless to themselves; like a sun-dial on the front of a house, to inform the neighbors and passengers, but not the owner within.

If a man would register all his opinions upon love, politics, religion, learning, &c., beginning from his youth, and so go on to old age, what a bundle of inconsistencies and contradictions would appear at last!

The stoical scheme of supplying our wants by lopping off our desires, is like cutting off our feet when we want shoes.

The reason why so few marriages are happy, is because young ladies spend their time in making nets, not in making cages.

The power of fortune is confessed only by the miserable; for the happy impute all their success to prudence or merit.

Ambition often puts men upon doing the meanest offices; so climbing is performed in the same posture with creeping.

Although men are accused for not knowing their own weakness, yet perhaps as few know their own strength. It is in men as in soils, where sometimes there is a vein of gold which the owner knows not of.

An idle reason lessens the weight of the good ones you gave before.

Arbitrary power is the natural object of temptation to a prince; as wine or women to a young fellow, or a bribe to a judge, or avarice to old age, or vanity to a woman.

The humor of exploding many things under the name of trifles, fopperies and only imaginary goods, is a very false proof either of wisdom or magnanimity, and a great check to virtuous actions. For instance, with regard to fame; there is in most people a reluctance and unwillingness to be forgotten. We observe, even among the vulgar, how fond they are to have an inscription over their grave. It requires but little philosophy to discover and observe that there is no intrinsic value in all this; however, if it be founded in our nature, as an incitement to virtue, it ought not to be ridiculed.

Complaint is the largest tribute Heaven receives, and the sincerest part of our devotion.

The common fluency of speech in many men, and most women, is owing to a scarcity of matter, and a scarcity of words; for whoever is a master of language, and hath a mind full of ideas, will be apt in speaking to hesitate upon the choice of both; whereas common speakers have only one set of ideas, and one set of words to clothe them in; and these are always ready at the mouth; so people come faster out of church when it is almost empty, than when a crowd is at the door.

To be vain is rather a mark of humility than pride. Vain men delight in telling what honors have been done them, what great company they have kept, and the like, by which they plainly confess that these honors were more than their due, and such as their friends would not believe if they had not been told: whereas a man truly proud thinks the greatest honors below his merit, and consequently scorns to boast. I therefore deliver it as a maxim, that whoever desires the character of a proud man ought to conceal his vanity.

I have known several persons of great fame for wisdom in public affairs and councils governed by foolish servants.

I have known great ministers, distinguished for wit and learning, who preferred none but dunces.

I have known men of great valor cowards to their wives.

I have known men of the greatest cunning perpetually cheated.

Dignity, high station, or great riches, are in some sort necessary to old men, in order to keep the younger at a distance, who are otherwise too apt to insult them upon the score of their age.

Every man desires to live long, but no man would be old.

Love of flattery, in most men, proceeds from the mean opinion they have of themselves; in women, from the contrary.

Kings are commonly said to have long hands; I wish they had as long ears.

Princes, in their infancy, childhood and youth, are said to discover prodigious parts and wit, to speak things that surprise and astonish: strange, so many hopeful princes, so many shameful kings! If they happen to die young, they would have been prodigies of wisdom and virtue: if they live, they are often prodigies, indeed, but of another sort.

Apollo was held the god of physic and sender of diseases. Both were originally the same trade, and still continue.

"That was excellently observed," said I, when I read a passage in an author where his opinion agrees with mine: when we differ, there I pronounce him to be mistaken.

Very few men, properly speaking, live at present; but are providing to live another time.

As universal a practice as lying is, and as easy a one as it seems, I do not remember to have heard three good lies in all my conversation, even from those who were most celebrated in that faculty.

ALGERNON C. SWINBURNE

(Harper & Brothers, Publishers)

ALGERNON CHARLES SWINBURNE was born near Henley, England, in 1837. He was educated at Eton and on the Continent. He began in his early youth to make the verses that, later, were to place him with the greatest poets of England. Among his best are: "The Queen Mother and Rosamond," "Atalanta in Calydon," "Bothwell," "Mary Stuart," "Songs of the Springtides," "Tristram of Lyonesse," "A Century of Roundels" and "Astrophel."

A MATCH

IF love were what the rose is,
    And I were like the leaf,
Our lives would grow together
In sad or singing weather,
Blown fields or flowerful closes,
    Green pleasure or gray grief;
If love were what the rose is,
    And I were like the leaf.

If I were what the words are,
    And love were like the tune,
With double sound and single
Delight our lips would mingle,
With kisses glad as birds are
    That get sweet rain at noon;
If I were what the words are,
    And love were like the tune.

If you were life, my darling,
   And I, your love, were death,
We'd shine and snow together
Ere March made sweet the weather
With daffodil and starling
   And hours of fruitful breath;
If you were life, my darling,
   And I, your love, were death.

If you were thrall to sorrow,
   And I were page to joy,
We'd play for lives and seasons,
With loving books and treasons,
And tears of night and morrow,
   And laughs of maid and boy;
If you were thrall to sorrow,
   And I were page to joy.

If you were April's lady,
   And I were lord in May,
We'd throw with leaves for hours,
And draw for days with flowers,
Till day, like night, were shady,
   And night were bright, like day;
If you were April's lady,
   And I were lord in May.

If you were queen of pleasure,
   And I were king of pain,
We'd hunt down love together,
Pluck out his flying-feather,
And teach his feet a measure,
   And find his mouth a rein;
If you were queen of pleasure,
   And I were king of pain.

THE GARDEN OF PROSERPINE

HERE, where the world is quiet;
    Here, where all trouble seems
Dead winds' and spent waves' riot
    In doubtful dreams of dreams;
I watch the green field growing
For reaping folk and sowing,
For harvest-time and mowing,
    A sleepy world of streams.

I am tired of tears and laughter,
    And men that laugh and weep
Of what may come hereafter
    For men that sow to reap:
I am weary of days and hours,
Blown buds of barren flowers,
Desires and dreams and powers
    And everything but sleep.

Here life has death for neighbor,
    And far from eye or ear
Wan waves and wet winds labor,
    Weak ships and spirits steer:
They drive adrift, and whither
They wot not who make thither;
But no such winds blow hither,
    And no such things grow here.

No growth of moor or coppice,
    No heather-flower or vine,
But bloomless buds of poppies,
    Green grapes of Proserpine;
Pale beds of blowing rushes
Where no leaf blooms or blushes,
Save this whereout she crushes
    For dead men deadly wine.

Pale, without name or number,
  In fruitless fields of corn,
They bow themselves and slumber
  All night till light is born;
And like a soul belated,
In hell and heaven unmated,
By cloud and mist abated
  Comes out of darkness morn.

Though one were strong as seven,
  He too with death shall dwell,
Nor wake with wings in heaven,
  Nor weep for pains in hell;
Though one were fair as roses,
His beauty clouds and closes;
And well though love reposes,
  In the end it is not well.

Pale, beyond porch and portal,
  Crowned with calm leaves, she stands
Who gathers all things mortal
  With cold immortal hands;
Her languid lips are sweeter
Than love's who fears to greet her,
To men that mix and meet her
  From many times and lands.

She waits for each and other,
  She waits for all men born;
Forgets the earth her mother,
  The life of fruits and corn;
And spring and seed and swallow
Take wing for her, and follow
Where summer song rings hollow
  And flowers are put to scorn.

THE GARDEN OF PROSERPINE

There go the loves that wither,
  The old loves with wearier wings;
And all dead years draw thither,
  And all disastrous things:
Dead dreams of days forsaken,
Blind buds that snows have shaken,
Wild leaves that winds have taken,
  Red strays of ruined springs.

We are not sure of sorrow,
  And joy was never sure;
To-day will die to-morrow;
  Time stoops to no man's lure;
And love, grown faint and fretful,
With lips but half regretful
Sighs, and with eyes forgetful
  Weeps that no loves endure.

From too much love of living,
  From hope and fear set free,
We thank with brief thanksgiving
  Whatever gods may be,
That no life lives forever;
That dead men rise up never;
That even the weariest river
  Winds somewhere safe to sea.

Then star nor sun shall waken,
  Nor any change of light:
Nor sound of waters shaken,
  Nor any sound or sight:
Nor winter leaves nor vernal,
Nor days nor things diurnal;
Only the sleep eternal
  In an eternal night.

IN MEMORY OF WALTER SAVAGE LANDOR

BACK to the flower-town, side by side,
  The bright months bring,
New-born, the bridegroom and the bride,
  Freedom and spring.

The sweet land laughs from sea to sea,
  Filled full of sun;
All things come back to her, being free—
  All things but one.

In many a tender wheaten plot,
  Flowers that were dead
Live, and old suns revive; but not
  That holier head.

By this white wandering waste of sea,
  Far north, I hear
One face shall never turn to me
  As once this year;

Shall never smile and turn and rest
  On mine as there,
Nor one most sacred hand be prest
  Upon my hair.

I came as one whose thoughts half linger
  Half run before;
The youngest to the oldest singer
  That England bore.

I found him whom I shall not find
  Till all grief end,
In holiest age our mightiest mind,
  Father and friend.

But thou, if anything endure,
   If hope there be,
O spirit that man's life left pure,
   Man's death set free,—

Not with disdain of days that were,
   Look earthward now:
Let dreams revive the reverend hair,
   The imperial brow:

Come back in sleep; for in the life
   Where thou art not
We find none like thee. Time and strife
   And the world's lot

Move thee no more; but love at least
   And reverend heart
May move thee, royal and released
   Soul, as thou art.

And thou, his Florence, to thy trust
   Receive and keep—
Keep safe his dedicated dust,
   His sacred sleep.

So shall thy lovers, come from far,
   Mix with thy name
As morning-star with evening-star
   His faultless fame.

OF SUCH IS THE KINGDOM OF HEAVEN

OF such is the kingdom of heaven: "
   No glory that ever was shed
From the crowning star of the seven
   That crowned the north world's head,

No word that ever was spoken
  Of human or godlike tongue,
Gave ever such godlike token
  Since human harps were strung.

No sign that ever was given
  To faithful or faithless eyes,
Showed ever beyond clouds riven
  So clear a Paradise.

Earth's creeds may be seventy times seven,
  And blood have defiled each creed:
If of such be the kingdom of heaven,
  It must be heaven indeed.

A FORSAKEN GARDEN

IN a coign of the cliff between lowland and high-
    land,
  At the sea-down's edge between windward and lee,
Walled round with rocks as in inland island,
  The ghost of a garden fronts the sea.
A girdle of brushwood and thorn incloses
  The steep square slope of the blossomless bed,
Where the weeds that grew green from the graves
      of its roses
          Now lie dead.

The fields fall southward, abrupt and broken,
  To the low last edge of the long lone land,
If a step should sound or a word be spoken,
  Would a ghost not rise at the strange guest's
      hand?
So long have the gray bare walks lain guestless,
  Through branches and briers if a man make way,
He shall find no life but the sea-wind's, restless
          Night and day.

The dense hard passage is blind and stifled,
    That crawls by a track none turn to climb
To the strait waste place that the years have **rifled**
    Of all but the thorns that are touched not of
        time.
The thorns he spares when the rose is taken;
    The rocks are left when he wastes the plain.
The wind that wanders, the weeds wind-shaken—
        These remain.

Not a flower to be pressed of the foot that falls **not**;
    As the heart of a dead man the seed-plots are **dry**;
From the thicket of thorns whence the nightingale
        calls not,
    Could she call, there were never a rose to reply.
Over the meadows that blossom and wither
    Rings but the notes of a sea-bird's song;
Only the sun and the rain come hither
        All year long.

The sun burns seer and the rain dishevels
    One gaunt bleak blossom of scentless breath;
Only the wind here hovers and revels
    In a round where life seems barren as death.
Here there was laughing of old, there was weeping,
    Haply, of lovers none ever will know,
Whose eyes went seaward a hundred sleeping
        Years ago.

Heart handfast in heart as they stood, "Look
        thither,"
    Did he whisper?—"look forth from the flowers to
        the sea;
For the foam flowers endure when the rose blossoms
        wither,
    And men that love lightly may die—but we?"
And the same wind sang and the same waves
        whitened,

139

And or ever the garden's last petals were shed,
In the lips that had whispered, the eyes that had
　　lightened,
　　　　Love was dead.
Or they loved their life through, and then went
　　whither?
　And were one to the end; but what end who
　　knows?
Love deep as the sea, as a rose must whither,—
　As the rose-red seaweed that mocks the rose.
Shall the dead take thought for the dead to love
　them?
　What love was ever as deep as a grave?
They are loveless now as the grass above them,
　　　　Or the wave.

All are at one now, roses and lovers,
　Not known of the cliffs and the fields and the sea;
Not a breath of the time that has been, hovers
　In the air now soft with a summer to be.
Not a breath shall there sweeten the seasons here-
　after
　Of the flowers or the lovers that laugh now or
　　weep,
When as they that are free now of weeping and
　laughter
　　　　We shall sleep.

Here death may deal not again for ever;
　Here change may come not till all change end.
From the graves they have made they shall rise up
　never,
　Who have left naught living to ravage and rend.
Earth, stones, and thorns of the wild ground
　growing,—
　While the sun and the rain live, these shall be;
Till a last wind's breath upon all these blowing
　　　　Roll the sea,

Till the slow sea rise and the sheer cliff crumble,
  Till terrace and meadow the deep gulfs drink,
Till the strength of the waves of the high tides
      humble
  The fields that lessen, the rocks that shrink.
Here now in his triumph where all things falter,
  Stretched out on the spoils, that his own hand
      spread,
As a God self-slain on his own strange altar,
      Death lies dead.

BAYARD TAYLOR

BAYARD TAYLOR, poet and novelist, was born in
Kennett Square, Chester County, Pa., in 1825; died
in Berlin, Germany, in 1878. He wrote a volume
of poems in 1844, and soon after secured a position
as a traveling newspaper correspondent in Europe.
During this trip he secured the material for his
famous "Views Afoot." Later he visited nearly
all the countries of Europe and the East, writing
sketches and travels. Among his best novels are
"Hannah Thurston" and "The Story of Kenneth."
He wrote many poems and a fine translation of
Goethe's "Faust."

BEDOUIN SONG

FROM the Desert I come to thee
   On a stallion shod with fire,
And the winds are left behind
   In the speed of my desire.
Under thy window I stand,
   And the midnight hears my cry:

I love thee, I love but thee,
   With a love that shall not die
     Till the sun grows cold,
     And the stars are old,
And the leaves of the Judgment-Book unfold!

Look from thy window and see
   My passion and my pain;
I lie on the sands below,
   And I faint in thy disdain.

Let the night-winds touch thy brow
  With the heat of my burning sigh,
And melt thee to hear the vow
  Of a love that shall not die
    Till the sun grows cold,
    And the stars are old,
And the leaves of the Judgment-Book unfold!

My steps are nightly driven
  By the fever in my breast,
To hear from thy lattice breathed
  The word that shall give me rest.
Open the door of thy heart,
  And open thy chamber door,
And my kisses shall teach thy lips
  The love that shall fade no more
    Till the sun grows cold,
    And the stars are old,
And the leaves of the Judgment-Book unfold!

AN INCIDENT IN THE CRIMEAN WAR

G IVE us a song!" the soldiers cried,
    The outer trenches guarding,
When the heated guns of the camp allied
  Grew weary of bombarding.

The dark Redan, in silent scoff,
  Lay grim and threatening under;
And the tawny mound of the Malakoff
  No longer belched its thunder.

There was a pause. A Guardsman said,
  "We storm the fort to-morrow;
Sing while we may; another day
  Will bring enough of sorrow."

They lay along the battery's side,
  Below the smoking cannon:
Brave hearts from Severn, and from Clyde,
  And from the banks of Shannon.

They sang of love, and not of fame;
  Forgot was Britain's glory;
Each heart recalled a different name,
  But all sang "Annie Laurie."

Voice after voice caught up the song,
  Until its tender passion
Rose like an anthem rich and strong—
  Their battle-eve confession.

Dear girl! Her name he dared not speak;
  But as the song grew louder,
Something upon the Soldier's cheek
  Washed off the stains of powder.

Beyond the darkening ocean burned
  The bloody sunset's embers,
While the Crimean valleys learned
  How English love remembers.

And once again a fire of hell
  Rained from the Russian quarters,
With scream of shot and burst of shell
  And bellowing of the mortars!

And Irish Nora's eyes are dim
  For a singer dumb and gory;
And English Mary mourns for him
  Who sang of "Annie Laurie."

Sleep, soldiers! still in honored rest,
  Your truth and valor wearing;
The bravest are the tenderest,
  The loving are the daring.

JEREMY TAYLOR

JEREMY TAYLOR, famous theologian, born in Cambridge, England, in 1613; died in Lisburn, Ireland, in 1667. He graduated from Oxford University and became a rector. He took the Royalist side in the English Civil War and lost his position. At the Restoration he was made Bishop of Down, Ireland. His most famous works were: "Rules and Exercises for Holy Living" and "Rules and Exercises for Holy Dying."

MARRIAGE

THE dominion of a man over his wife is no other than as the soul rules the body; for which it takes a mighty care, and uses it with a delicate tenderness, and cares for it in all contingencies, and watches to keep it from all evils, and studies to make for it fair provisions, and very often is led by its inclinations and desires, and does never contradict its appetites, but when they are evil, and then also not without some trouble and sorrow; and its government comes only to this—it furnishes the body with light and understanding, and the body furnishes the soul with hands and feet; the soul governs, because the body cannot else be happy, but the government is no other than provision; as a nurse governs a child when she causes him to eat, and to be warm, and dry, and quiet. And yet even the very government itself is divided; for man and wife in the family, are as the sun and moon in the firmament of heaven; he rules by day, and she by night—that is, in the lesser and more proper

145

circles of her affairs, in the conduct of domestic provisions and necessary offices, and shines only by his light, and rules by his authority. And as the moon in opposition to the sun shines brightest; that is, then, when she is in her own circles and separate regions; so is the authority of the wife then most conspicuous, when she is separate and in her proper sphere; "in gynæceo," in the nursery, and offices of domestic employment. But when she is in conjunction with the sun, her brother, that is, in that place and employment in which his care and proper offices are employed, her light is not seen, her authority hath no proper business. But else there is no difference, for they were barbarous people, among whom wives were instead of servants; and it is a sign of weakness to force the camels to kneel for their load because thou hast not strength and spirit enough to climb; to make the affections and evenness of a wife bend by the flexures of a servant is a sign the man is not wise enough to govern when another is by. And as amongst men and women humility is the way to be preferred, so it is in husbands, they shall prevail by cession, by sweetness and counsel, and charity and compliance. So that we cannot discourse of the man's right without describing the measures of his duty.

ALFRED TENNYSON

ALFRED TENNYSON, Poet Laureate of England, was born in Somersby, Lincolnshire, in 1809; died at Aldworth House, Surrey, in 1892. At eight he wrote verses modelled on Thomson's "Season's"; at fourteen a drama in blank verse. In 1828 he entered Trinity College, Cambridge, and the following year won a medal for his prize poem, "Timbuctoo." After leaving college he wrote a large number of poems, but fame did not come until in 1842, when he published two volumes. After writing "The Princess" and "In Memoriam" he was appointed Poet Laureate. The appointment came through the Prince Consort, who considered "In Memoriam" one of the greatest poems ever written. In 1883 he was made Baron Tennyson d'Eyncourt. Among his best poems are "Maud," "The Idyls of the King," "Enoch Arden" and "Locksley Hall."

BUGLE SONG

(From "The Princess")

THE splendor falls on castle walls
   And snowy summits old in story;
The long light shakes across the lakes,
   And the wild cataract leaps in glory.
Blow, bugle, blow, set the wild echoes flying;
Blow, bugle; answer, echoes, dying, dying, dying.

O hark, O hear! how thin, how clear,
   And thinner, clearer, farther going!
O sweet and far from cliff and scar
   The horns of Elfland faintly blowing!
Blow, let us hear the purple glens replying;
Blow, bugle; answer echoes, dying, dying, dying.

O love, they die in yon rich sky,
    They faint on hill or field or river;
Our echoes roll from soul to soul,
    And grow forever and forever.
Blow, bugle, blow; set the wild echoes flying,
And answer, echoes, answer, dying, dying, dying

BREAK, BREAK, BREAK!

BREAK, break, break
    On thy cold gray stones, O Sea!
And I would that my tongue could utter
    The thoughts that arise in me.

O well for the fisherman's boy,
    That he shouts with his sister at play!
O well for the sailor-lad,
    That he sings in his boat on the bay!

And the stately ships go on
    To their haven under the hill;
But O for the touch of a vanished hand
    And the sound of a voice that is still!

Break, break, break
    At the foot of thy crags, O Sea!
But the tender grace of a day that is dead
    Will never come back to me.

RING OUT, WILD BELLS
(From "In Memoriam")

RING out, wild bells, to the wild sky,
    The flying cloud, the frosty light;
The year is dying in the night;
Ring out, wild bells, and let him die.

RING OUT, WILD BELLS

Ring out the old, ring in the new,
  Ring, happy bells, across the snow;
  The year is going, let him go;
Ring out the false, ring in the true.

Ring out the grief that saps the mind,
  For those that here we see no more;
  Ring out the feud of rich and poor,
Ring in redress to all mankind.

Ring out a slowly dying cause,
  And ancient forms of party strife;
  Ring in the nobler modes of life,
With sweeter manners, purer laws.

Ring out the want, the care, the sin,
  The faithless coldness of the time;
  Ring out, ring out, my mournful rhymes.
But ring the fuller minstrel in.

Ring out false pride in place and blood,
  The civic slander and the spite;
  Ring in the love of truth and right,
Ring in the commmon love of good.

Ring out old shapes of foul disease;
  Ring out the narrowing lust of gold;
  Ring out the thousand wars of old,
Ring in the thousand years of peace.

Ring in the valiant man and free,
  The larger heart, the kindlier hand;
  Ring out the darkness of the land,
Ring in the Christ that is to be.

COME INTO THE GARDEN MAUD

(From "Maud")

COME into the garden, Maud,
    For the black bat, night, has flown!
Come into the garden, Maud,
  I am here at the gate alone;
And the woodbine spices are wafted abroad,
  And the musk of the rose is blown.

For a breeze of morning moves,
  And the planet of Love is on high,
Beginning to faint in the light that she loves,
  On a bed of daffodil sky,—
To faint in the light of the sun she loves,
  To faint in his light, and to die.

All night have the roses heard
  The flute, violin, bassoon;
All night has the casement jessamine stirr'd
  To the dancers dancing in tune,—
Till a silence fell with the waking bird,
  And a hush with the setting moon.

I said to the lily, "There is but one
  With whom she has heart to be gay.
When will the dancers leave her alone?
  She is weary of dance and play."
Now half to the setting moon are gone,
  And half to the rising day;
Low on the sand and loud on the stone
  The last wheel echoes away.

I said to the rose, "The brief night goes
  In babble and revel and wine.
O young lord-lover, what sighs are those
  For one that will never be thine?
But mine, but mine," so I sware to the rose,
  "For ever and ever mine!"

And the soul of the rose went into my blood,
  As the music clash'd in the hall;
And long by the garden lake I stood,
  For I heard your rivulet fall
From the lake to the meadow and on to the wood,
  Our wood, that is dearer than all;

From the meadow your walks have left so sweet
  That whenever a March wind sighs,
He sets the jewel-print of your feet
  In violets blue as your eyes,
To the woody hollows in which we meet,
  And the valleys of Paradise.

The slender acacia would not shake
  One long milk-bloom on the tree;
The white lake-blossom fell into the lake,
  As the pimpernel dozed on the lea;
But the rose was awake all night for your sake,
  Knowing your promise to me;
The lilies and roses were all awake,
  They sigh'd for the dawn and thee.

Queen rose of the rosebud garden of girls,
  Come hither, the dances are done,
In gloss of satin and glimmer of pearls,
  Queen lily and rose in one;
Shine out, little head, sunning over with curls,
  To the flowers, and be their sun.

There has fallen a splendid tear
  From the passion-flower at the gate.
She is coming, my dove, my dear;
  She is coming, my life, my fate!
The red rose cries, "She is near, she is near;"
  And the white rose weeps, "She is late;"
The larkspur listens, "I hear, I hear;"
  And the lily whispers, "I wait."

She is coming, my own, my sweet!
  Were it ever so airy a tread,
My heart would hear her and beat,
  Were it earth in an earthy bed;
My dust would hear her and beat,
  Had I lain for a century dead;
Would startle and tremble under her feet,
  And blossom in purple and red.

COME DOWN, O MAID

COME down, O maid, from yonder mountain
    height:
What pleasure lives in height (the shepherd sang),
In height and cold, the splendor of the hills?
But cease to move so near the Heavens, and cease
To glide, a sunbeam, by the blasted pine,
To sit, a star, upon the sparkling spire;
And come, for love is of the valley, come,
For love is of the valley; come thou down
And find him; by the happy threshold he,
Or hand in hand with Plenty in the maize,
Or red with spirted purple of the vats,
Or foxlike in the vine; nor cares to walk
With Death and Morning on the Silver Horns,
Nor wilt thou snare him in the white ravine,
Nor find him dropt upon the firths of ice,
That, huddling, slant in furrow-cloven falls,
To roll the torrent out of dusky doors:
But follow: let the torrent dance thee down
To find him in the valley; let the wild,
Lean-headed eagles yelp alone, and leave
The monstrous ledges there to slope, and spill
Their thousand wreaths of dangling water-smoke,
That, like a broken purpose, waste in air:
So waste not thou; but come; for all the vales
Await thee; azure pillars of the hearth

Arise to thee; the children call, and I,
Thy shepherd, pipe, and sweet is every sound.
Sweeter thy voice, but every sound is sweet;
Myriads of rivulets hurrying thro' the lawn,
The moan of doves in immemorial elms,
And murmuring of innumerable bees."

THE CHARGE OF THE LIGHT BRIGADE

HALF a league, half a league,
  Half a league onward,
All in the valley of Death
Rode the six hundred.
"Forward, the Light Brigade!
Charge for the guns!" he said:
Into the valley of Death
  Rode the six hundred.

"Forward, the Light Brigade!"
Was there a man dismay'd?
Not though the soldier knew
  Some one had blunder'd:
Their's not to make reply,
Their's not to reason why,
Their's but to do and die:
Into the valley of Death
  Rode the six hundred.

Cannon to right of them,
Cannon to left of them,
Cannon in front of them
  Volley'd and thunder'd;
Storm'd at with shot and shell,
Boldly they rode and well,
Into the jaws of Death,
Into the mouth of Hell,
  Rode the six hundred:

Flash'd all their sabres bare,
Flash'd as they turn'd in air,
Sabring the gunners there,
Charging an army, while
  All the world wonder'd:
Plunged in the battery-smoke,
Right through the line they broke;
  Cossack and Russian
Reel'd from the sabre-stroke
  Shatter'd and sunder'd.
Then they rode back, but not—
  Not the six hundred.

Cannon to right of them,
Cannon to left of them,
Cannon behind them
  Volley'd and thunder'd;
Storm'd at with shot and shell,
While horse and hero fell,
They that had fought so well,
Came through the jaws of Death
Back from the mouth of Hell,
All that was left of them,
  Left of six hundred.

When can their glory fade?
Oh, the wild charge they made!
  All the world wonder'd.
Honor the charge they made!
Honor the Light Brigade,
  Noble six hundred!

THE RECONCILIATION

AS thro' the land at eve we went,
    And pluck'd the ripen'd ears,
We fell out, my wife and I,
We fell out—I know not why—

And kiss'd again with tears.
And blessings on the falling-out
    That all the more endears,
When we fall out with those we love
    And kiss again with tears!
For when we came where lies the child
    We lost in others years,
There above the little grave,
Oh there above the little grave,
    We kiss'd again with tears.

HOME THEY BROUGHT HER WARRIOR DEAD

HOME they brought her warrior dead:
    She nor swoon'd, nor utter'd cry:
All her maidens, watching, said,
    "She must weep or she will die."

Then they praised him, soft and low,
Called him worthy to be loved,
Truest friend and noblest foe;
    Yet she neither spoke nor moved.

Stole a maiden from her place,
    Lightly to the warrior stept,
Took the face-cloth from the face;
    Yet she neither moved nor wept.

Rose a nurse of ninety years,
    Set his child upon her knee—
Like summer tempest came her tears—
    "Sweet my child, I live for thee."

TEARS, IDLE TEARS

(From "The Princess")

TEARS, idle tears, I know not what they mean,
 Tears from the depth of some divine despair
Rise in the heart, and gather to the eyes,
In looking on the happy autumn fields,
And thinking of the days that are no more.

Fresh as the first beam glittering on a sail,
That brings our friends up from the under-world,
Sad as the last which reddens over one
That sinks with all we love below the verge;
So sad, so fresh, the days that are no more.

Ah, sad and strange as in dark summer dawns
The earliest pipe of half-awaken'd birds
To dying ears, when unto dying eyes
The casement slowly grows a glimmering square;
So sad, so strange, the days that are no more.

Dear as remember'd kisses after death,
And sweet as those by hopeless fancy feign'd
On lips that are for others: deep as love,
Deep as first love, and wild with all regret;
Oh, death in life! the days that are no more.

THE DEATH OF THE OLD YEAR

FULL knee-deep lies the winter snow,
 And the winter winds are wearily sighing:
Toll ye the church-bell, sad and slow,
And tread softly and speak low;
 For the old year lies a-dying.

Old year, you must not die;
    You came to us so readily,
    You lived with us so steadily;
        Old year, you shall not die.

He lieth still; he doth not move;
    He will not see the dawn of day;
He hath no other life above;
He gave me a friend, and a true, true love,
    And the New-year will take them away.
        Old year, you must not go;
    So long as you have been with us,
    Such joy as you have seen with us,—
        Old year, you shall not go.

He frothed his bumpers to the brim;
    A jollier year we shall not see.
But though his eyes are waxing dim,
And though his foes speak ill of him,
    He was a friend to me.
        Old year, you shall not die;
    We did so laugh and cry with you,
    I've half a mind to die with you,
        Old year, if you must die.

He was full of joke and jest;
    But all his merry quips are o'er.
To see him die, across the waste
His son and heir doth ride post haste,
    But he'll be dead before.
        Every one for his own.
    The night is starry and cold, my friend,
    And the New-year blithe and bold, my friend,
        Comes up to take his own.

How hard he breathes! o'er the snow
  I heard just now the crowing cock.
The shadows flicker to and fro.
The cricket chirps, the light burns low,—
  'Tis nearly twelve o'clock.
    Shake hands before you die.
  Old year, we'll dearly rue for you.
  What is it we can do for you?—
    Speak out before you die.

His face is growing sharp and thin;—
  Alack! our friend is gone.
Close up his eyes, tie up his chin,
Step from the corpse, and let him in
  Who standeth there alone,
    And waiteth at the door.
  There's a new foot on the floor, my friend,
  And a new face at the door, my friend,
    A new face at the door.

SONG OF THE BROOK

I COME from haunts of coot and hern:
  I make a sudden sally
And sparkle out among the fern,
  To bicker down a valley.

By thirty hills I hurry down,
  Or slip between the ridges;
By twenty thorps, a little town,
  And half a hundred bridges.

Till last by Philip's farm I flow
  To join the brimming river;
For men may come and men may go,
  But I go on for ever.

I chatter over stony ways,
  In little sharps and trebles;
I bubble into eddying bays,
  I babble on the pebbles.

With many a curve my banks I fret
  By many a field and fallow,
And many a fairy foreland set
  With willow-weed and mallow.

I chatter, chatter, as I flow
  To join the brimming river;
For men may come and men may go,
  But I go on for ever.

I wind about, and in and out,
  With here a blossom sailing,
And here and there a lusty trout,
  And here and there a grayling.

And here and there a foamy flake
  Upon me, as I travel,
With many a silvery waterbreak
  Above the golden gravel;

And draw them all along, and flow
  To join the brimming river;
For men may come and men may go,
  But I go on for ever.

I steal by lawns and grassy plots;
  I slide by hazel covers;
I move the sweet forget-me-nots
  That grow for happy lovers.

I slip, I slide, I gloom, I glance,
  Among my skimming swallows,
I make the netted sunbeam dance
  Against my sandy shallows.

I murmur under moon and stars
In brambly wildernesses;
I linger by my shingly bars;
I loiter round my cresses;

And out again I curve and flow
To join the brimming river;
For men may come and men may go,
But I go on for ever.

ASK ME NO MORE

ASK me no more: the moon may draw the sea;
The cloud may stoop from heaven and take
the shape,
With fold to fold, of mountain or of cape;
But, oh too fond, when have I answer'd thee?
Ask me no more.

Ask me no more: what answer should I give?
I love not hollow cheek or faded eye;
Yet, O my friend, I will not have thee die!
Ask me no more, lest I should bid thee live;
Ask me no more.

Ask me no more: thy fate and mine are seal'd.
I strove against the stream, and all in vain.
Let the great river take me to the main.
No more, dear love, for at a touch I yield;
Ask me no more!

DE PROFUNDIS

OUT of the Deep, my child, out of the Deep:
Where all that was to be in all that was
Whirled for a million æons through the vast,
Waste dawn of multitudinous eddying light—

Out of the Deep, my child, out of the Deep!
Through all this changing world of changeless law,
And every phase of ever heightening life,
And nine long months of ante-natal gloom,
With this last moon, this crescent—her dark orb
Touched with earth's light—thou comest, Darling
    Boy;
Our Own; a babe in lineament and limb
Perfect, and prophet of the perfect man;
Whose face and form are hers and mine in one,
Indissolubly married, like our love;
Live and be happy in thyself, and serve
This mortal race, thy kin, so well that men
May bless thee, as we bless thee, O young life,
Breaking with laughter from the dark; and may
The fated channel where thy motion lives
Be prosperously shaped, and sway thy course
Along the years of haste and random youth
Unshattered—then full current through full man;
And last, in kindly curves, with gentlest fall,
By quiet fields, a slowly dying power,
To that last Deep where we and thou are still.

ST. AGNES' EVE

DEEP on the convent-roof the snows
    Are sparkling to the moon:
My breath to heaven like vapor goes:
    May my soul follow soon!

The shadows of the convent-towers
    Slant down the snowy sward,
Still creeping with the creeping hours
    That lead me to my Lord:
Make Thou my spirit pure and clear
    As are the frosty skies,
Or this first snowdrop of the year
    That in my bosom lies.

As these white robes are soil'd and dark,
  To yonder shining ground;
As this pale taper's earthly spark,
  To yonder argent round;
So shows my soul before the Lamb,
  My spirit before Thee;
So in mine earthly house I am,
  To that I hope to be.
Break up the heavens, O Lord! and far,
  Thro' all yon starlight keen,
Draw me, thy bride, a glittering star,
  In raiment white and clean.

He lifts me to the golden doors;
  The flashes come and go;
All heaven bursts her starry floors,
  And strews her lights below,
And deepens on and up! the gates
  Roll back, and far within
For me the Heavenly Bridegroom waits,
  To make me pure of sin.
The sabbaths of Eternity,
  One sabbath deep and wide—
A light upon the shining sea—
  The Bridegroom with his bride!

THE MAY QUEEN

YOU must wake and call me early, call me early,
  mother dear;
To-morrow 'ill be the happiest time of all the glad
  New-year;
Of all the glad New-year, mother, the maddest, mer-
  riest day;
For I'm to be Queen o' the May, mother, I'm to be
  Queen o' the May.

There's many a black black eye, they say, but none
    so bright as mine;
There's Margaret and Mary, there's Kate and Caro-
    line:
But none so fair as little Alice in all the land, they
    say,
So I'm to be Queen o' the May mother, I'm to be
    Queen o' the May.

I sleep so sound all night, mother, that I shall never
    wake,
If you do not call me loud, when the day begins to
    break:
But I must gather knots of flowers, and buds and
    garlands gay,
For I'm to be Queen o' the May, mother, I'm to be
    Queen o' the May.

As I came up the valley, whom think ye should I
    see,
But Robin leaning on the bridge beneath the hazel
    tree?
He thought of that sharp look, mother, I gave him
    yesterday—
But I'm to be Queen o' the May, mother, I'm to be
    Queen o' the May.

He thought I was a ghost, mother, for I was all in
    white,
And I ran by him without speaking, like a flash of
    light.
They call me cruel-hearted, but I care not what they
    say,
For I'm to be Queen o' the May, mother, I'm to be
    Queen o' the May.

They say he's dying all for love, but that can never
be:
They say his heart is breaking, mother—what is that
to me?
There's many a bolder lad 'ill woo me any summer
day,
And I'm to be Queen o' the May, mother, I'm to
be Queen o' the May.

Little Effie shall go with me to-morrow to the green,
And you'll be there, too, mother, to see me made the
queen;
For the shepherd lads on every side 'ill come from
far away,
And I'm to be Queen o' the May, mother, I'm to be
Queen o' the May.

The honeysuckle round the porch has wov'n its wavy
bowers,
And by the meadow-trenches blow the faint sweet
cuckoo-flowers;
And the wild marsh-marigold shines like fire in
swamps and hollows gray,
And I'm to be Queen o' the May, mother, I'm to be
Queen o' the May.

The night winds come and go, mother, upon the
meadow grass,
And the happy stars above them seem to brighten as
they pass;
There will not be a drop of rain the whole of the
livelong day,
And I'm to be Queen o' the May, mother, I'm to be
Queen o' the May.

All the valley, mother, 'ill be fresh and green and
still,
And the cowslip and the crowfoot are over all the
hill,

And the rivulet in the flowery dale 'ill merrily glance
    and play,
For I'm to be Queen o' the May, mother, I'm to be
    Queen o' the May.

So you must wake and call me early, call me early,
    mother dear,
To-morrow 'ill be the happiest time of all the glad
    New-year:
To-morrow 'ill be of all the year the maddest, mer-
    riest day,
For I'm to be Queen o' the May, mother, I'm to be
    Queen o' the May.

THE LADY OF SHALOTT

I

ON either side the river lie
    Long folds of barley and of rye,
That clothe the wold and meet the sky;
And thro' the field the road runs by
    To many-towered Camelot;
And up and down the people go,
Gazing where the lilies blow
Round an island there below,
    The island of Shalott.

Willows whiten, aspens quiver,
Little breezes dusk and shiver
Thro' the wave that runs forever,
By the island in the river
    Flowing down to Camelot.
Four gray walls, and four gray towers,
Overlook a space of flowers,
And the silent sea imbowers
    The Lady of Shalott.

By the margin, willow-veil'd
Slide the heavy barges, trail'd
By slow horses; and unhail'd
The shallop flitteth, silken-sail'd,
    Skimming down to Camelot:
But who hath seen her wave her hand?
Or at the casement, seen her stand?
Or is she known in all the land
    The Lady of Shalott?

Only reapers, reaping early
In among the bearded barley,
Hear a song that echoes cheerly
From the river winding clearly
    Down to tower'd Camelot;
And by the moon the reaper weary,
Piling sheaves in uplands airy,
Listening, whispers, " 'Tis the fairy
    Lady of Shalott."

II

There she weaves by night and day
A magic web with colors gay.
She has heard a whisper say,
A curse is on her if she stay
    To look down to Camelot.
She knows not what the curse may be,
And so she weaveth steadily,
And little other care hath she,
    The Lady of Shalott.

And moving through a mirror clear
That hangs before her all the year,
Shadows of the world appear.
There she sees the highway near,
    Winding down to Camelot;

There the river-eddy whirls,
And there the surly village churls
And the red cloaks of market-girls,
    Pass onward from Shalott.

Sometimes a troop of damsels glad,
An abbot or an ambling pad,
Sometimes a curly shepherd-lad,
Or long-hair'd page in crimson clad,
    Goes by to tower'd Camelot;
And sometimes thro' the mirror blue
The knights come riding, two and two;
She hath no loyal knight and true.
    The Lady of Shalott.

But in her web she still delights
To weave the mirror's magic sights;
For often, thro' the silent nights,
A funeral, with plumes and lights,
    And music, went to Camelot;
Or when the moon was overhead,
Came two young lovers lately wed:
"I am half-sick of shadows," said
    The Lady of Shalott.

III

A bow-shot from her bower-eaves,
He rode between the barley-sheaves;
The sun came dazzling through the leaves,
And flamed upon the brazen greaves
    Of bold Sir Lancelot.
A red-cross knight forever kneeled
To a lady in his shield,
That sparkled on the yellow field,
    Beside remote Shalott.

The gemmy bridle glitter'd free,
Like to some branch of stars we see
Hung in the golden galaxy;
The bridle-bells rang merrily
    As he rode down to Camelot:
And from his blazoned baldric slung
A mighty silver bugle hung,
And as he rode his armor rung,
    Beside remote Shalott.

All in the blue, unclouded weather
Thick-jewell'd shone the saddle-leather,
The helmet and the helmet-feather
Burned like one burning flame together
    As he rode down to Camelot.
As often thro' the purple night,
Below the starry clusters bright,
Some bearded meteor, trailing light,
    Moves over still Shalott.

His broad, clear brow in sunlight glow'd;
On burnish'd hooves his war-horse trode;
From underneath his helmet flow'd
His coal-black curls as on he rode,
    As he rode down to Camelot.
From the bank and from the river
He flashed into the crystal mirror,
"Tirra lirra," by the river
    Sang Sir Lancelot.

She left the web, she left the loom,
She made three paces thro' the room,
She saw the water-lily bloom,
She saw the helmet and the plume,
    She look'd down to Camelot.
Out flew the web and floated wide;
The mirror crack'd from side to side;
"The curse is come upon me," cried
    The Lady of Shalott.

In the stormy east-wind straining,
The pale yellow woods are waning,
The broad stream in his banks complaining,
Heavily the low sky raining
    Over tower'd Camelot;
Down she came and found a boat
Beneath a willow left afloat,
And round about the prow she wrote
    The Lady of Shalott.

And down the river's dim expanse—
Like some bold seer in a trance,
Seeing all his own mischance—
With a glassy countenance
    Did she look to Camelot.
And at the closing of the day
She loosed the chain and down she lay;
The broad stream bore her far away,
    The Lady of Shalott.

Lying, robed in snowy white
That loosely flew to left and right—
That leaves upon her falling light—
Thro' the noises of the night
    She floated down to Camelot:
And as the boat-head wound along
The willow hills and fields among
They heard her singing her last song,
    The Lady of Shalott.

Heard a carol, mournful, holy,
Chanted loudly, chanted lowly,
Till her blood was frozen slowly,
And her eyes were darken'd wholly,
    Turn'd to tower'd Camelot;
For ere she reach'd upon the tide
The first house by the water-side,
Singing in her song she died,
    The Lady of Shalott.

Under tower and balcony,
By garden-wall and gallery,
A gleaming shape she floated by,
A corse between the houses high,
    Silent into Camelot.
Out upon the wharves they came,
Knight and burgher, lord and dame,
And round the prow they read her name,
    The Lady of Shalott.

Who is this? and what is here?
And in the lighted palace near
Died the sound of royal cheer:
And they crossed themselves for fear,
    All the knights of Camelot:
But Lancelot mused a little space:
He said, "She has a lovely face:
God in his mercy lend her grace,
    The Lady of Shalott."

ENOCH ARDEN'S DYING MESSAGE

(From "Enoch Arden")

                  As the woman heard
Fast flowed the current of her easy tears,
While in her heart she yearn'd incessantly
To rush abroad all round the little haven,
Proclaiming Enoch Arden and his woes;
But awed and promise-bounden she forebore,
Saying only: "See your bairns before you go!
Eh, let me fetch 'em, Arden," and arose
Eager to bring them down, for Enoch hung
A moment on her words, but then replied:
    "Woman, disturb me not now at the last,
But let me hold my purpose till I die.
Sit down again; mark me and understand
While I have power to speak. I charge you now,
When you shall see her, tell her that I died

Blessing her, praying for her, loving her;
As when she laid her head beside my own.
And tell my daughter Annie, whom I saw
So like her mother, that my latest breath
Was spent in blessing her and praying for her.
And tell my son that I died blessing him.
And say to Philip that I blest him, too:
He never meant us anything but good.
But if my children care to see me dead,
Who hardly knew me living, let them come,
I am their father; but she must not come,
For my dead face would vex her after-life.
And now there is but one of all my blood
Who will embrace me in the world-to-be:
This hair is his: she cut it off and gave it,
And I have borne it with me all these years,
And thought to bear it with me to my grave;
But now my mind is changed, for I shall see him,
My babe, in bliss. Wherefore, when I am gone,
Take, give her this, for it will comfort her;
It will moreover be a token to her
That I am he. . . . ."
    The third night after this,
While Enoch slumbered, motionless and pale,
And Miriam watched and dozed at intervals,
There came so loud a calling of the sea
That all the houses of the harbor rang.
He woke, he rose, he spread his arms abroad,
Crying with a loud voice, "A sail! a sail!
I am saved!" and so fell back and spoke no more.

LADY CLARA VERE DE VERE

LADY Clara Vere de Vere,
    Of me you shall not win renown;
You thought to break a country heart
    For pastime, ere you went to town.

At me you smiled, but unbeguiled
   I saw the snare, and I retired:
The daughter of a hundred Earls,
   You are not one to be desired.

Lady Clara Vere de Vere,
   I know you're proud to bear your name,
Your pride is yet no mate for mine,
   Too proud to care from whence I came.
Nor would I break for your sweet sake.
   A heart that dotes on truer charms.
A simple maiden in her flower
   Is worth a hundred coats-of-arms.

Lady Clara Vere de Vere,
   Some meeker pupil you must find,
For were you queen of all that is,
   I could not stoop to such a mind.
You sought to prove how I could love,
   And my disdain is my reply.
The lion on your old stone gates
   Is not more cold to you than I.

Lady Clara Vere de Vere,
   You put strange memories in my head.
Not thrice your branching limes have blown
   Since I beheld young Laurence dead.
Oh, your sweet eyes, your low replies:
   A great enchantress you may be;
But there was that across his throat
   Which you had hardly cared to see.

Lady Clara Vere de Vere,
   When thus he met his mother's view,
She had the passions of her kind,
   She spake some certain truths of you.
Indeed, I heard one bitter word
   That scarce is fit for you to hear;
Her manners had not that repose
   Which stamps the caste of Vere de Vere.

Lady Clara Vere de Vere,
    There stands a specter in your hall:
The guilt of blood is at your door:
    You changed a wholesome heart to gall.
You held your course without remorse,
    To make him trust his modest worth,
And, last, you fixed a vacant stare,
    And slew him with your noble birth.

Trust, me, Clara Vere de Vere,
    From yon blue heavens above us bent,
The grand old gardener and his wife
    Smile at the claims of long descent.
Howe'er it be, it seems to me,
    'Tis only noble to be good.
Kind hearts are more than coronets,
    And simple faith than Norman blood.

I know you, Clara Vere de Vere:
    You pine among your halls and towers:
The languid light of your proud eyes
    Is wearied of the rolling hours.
In glowing health, with boundless wealth,
    But sickening of a vague disease,
You know so ill to deal with time,
    You needs must play such pranks as these.

Clara, Clara Vere de Vere,
    If time be heavy on your hands,
Are there no beggars at your gate,
    Nor any poor about your lands?
Oh teach the orphan boy to read,
    Or teach the orphan girl to sew,
Pray heaven for a human heart,
    And let the foolish yeoman go.

ENOCH ARDEN AT THE WINDOW

(From " Enoch Arden ")

BUT Enoch yearned to see her face again;
  " If I might look on her sweet face again
And know that she is happy." So the thought
Haunted and harassed him and drove him forth
At evening when the dull November day
Was growing duller twilight, to the hill.
There he sat down gazing on all below:
There did a thousand memories roll upon him
Unspeakable for sadness. By and by
The ruddy square of comfortable light,
Far-blazing from the rear of Philip's house,
Allured him, as the beacon-blaze allures
The bird of passage, till he madly strike
Against it, and beats out his weary life.

For Philip's dwelling fronted on the street,
The latest house to landward; but behind,
With one small gate that opened on the waste,
Flourished a little garden square and walled:
And in it throve an ancient evergreen,
A yew-tree, and all around it ran a walk
Of shingle, and a walk divided it:
But Enoch shunned the middle walk and stole
Up by the wall, behind the yew; and thence
That which he better might have shunned, if griefs
Like his have worse or better, Enoch saw.

For cups and silver on the burnished board
Sparkled and shone; so genial was the hearth;
And on the right hand of the hearth he saw
Philip, the slighted suitor of old times,
Stout, rosy, with his babe across his knees;
And o'er her second father stoopt a girl,
A later but a loftier Annie Lee,

Fair-haired and tall, and from her lifted hand
Dangled a length of ribbon and a ring
To tempt the babe, who reared his creasy arms,
Caught at and ever missed it, and they laughed:
And on the left hand of the hearth he saw
The mother glancing often at her babe,
But turning now and then to speak with him,
Her son, who stood beside her tall and strong,
And saying that which pleased him, for he smiled.

Now when the dead man come to life beheld
His wife his wife no more, and saw the babe
Hers, yet not his, upon the father's knee,
And all the warmth, the peace, the happiness,
And his own children tall and beautiful,
And him, that other, reigning in his place,
Lord of his rights and of his children's love,—
Then he, though Miriam Lane had told him all,
Because things seen are mightier than things heard,
Staggered and shook, holding the branch, and feared
To send abroad a shrill and terrible cry,
Which in one moment, like the blast of doom,
Would shatter all the happiness of the hearth.

He therefore turning softly like a thief,
Lest the harsh shingle should grate underfoot,
And feeling all along the garden-wall,
Lest he should swoon and tumble and be found,
Crept to the gate, and opened it, and closed,
As lightly as a sick man's chamber-door,
Behind him, and came out upon the waste.

And there he would have knelt, but that his knees
Were feeble, so that falling prone he dug
His fingers into the wet earth, and prayed.

WELCOME TO ALEXANDRA
(March 7, 1863)

SEA-KING'S daughter from over the sea,
            Alexandra!
Saxon and Norman and Dane are we,
But all of us Danes in our welcome of thee,
            Alexandra!

Welcome her, thunders of fort and of fleet!
Welcome her, thundering cheer of the street!
Welcome her, all things youthful and sweet,
Scatter the blossom under her feet!
Break, happy land, into earlier flowers!
Make music, O bird, in the new-budded bowers!
Blazon your mottoes of blessing and prayer!
Welcome her, welcome her, all that is ours!
Warble, O bugle, and trumpet, blare!
Flags, flutter out upon turrets and towers!
Flames, on the windy headland flare!
Utter your jubilee, steeple and spire!
Clash, ye bells, in the merry March air!
Flash, ye cities, in rivers of fire!
Rush to the roof, sudden rocket, and higher
Melt into the stars for the land's desire!
Roll and rejoice, jubilant voice,
Roll as the ground-swell dashed on the strand,
Roar as the sea when he welcomes the land,
And welcome her, welcome the land's desire,
The sea-king's daughter, as happy as fair,
Blissful bride of a blissful heir,
Bride of the heir of the kings of the sea—
O joy to the people and joy to the throne,
Come to us, love us, and make us your own;
For Saxon or Dane or Norman we,
Teuton or Celt, or whatever we be,
We are each all Dane in our welcome of thee,
            Alexandra!

SWEET AND LOW
(From " The Princess ")

SWEET and low, sweet and low,
  Wind of the western sea,
Low, low, breathe and blow,
  Wind of the western sea!
Over the rolling waters go,
Come from the dying moon, and blow,
  Blow him again to me;
While my little one, while my pretty one sleeps.

Sleep and rest, sleep and rest,
  Father will come to thee soon;
Rest, rest, on mother's breast,
  Father will come to thee soon;
Father will come to his babe in the nest,
Silver sails all out of the west
  Under the silver moon;
Sleep, my little one, sleep, my pretty one, sleep.

177

WILLIAM M. THACKERAY

WILLIAM MAKEPEACE THACKERAY, born of English parents in Calcutta, India, 1811; died in London in 1863. He went to Cambridge, but did not take a degree. He studied art, but made little use of the accomplishment beyond the illustration of his books. He early turned to literature, and earned a reputation that placed him by the side of Dickens and Walter Scott. Unlike his great rival, Dickens, he gained popularity slowly. He excelled in satire, which feature of his writings somewhat obscured the benevolent nature of the man and of his philosophy. No greater work was done in the domain of English fiction in the nineteenth century than the creation of Becky Sharp and Colonel Newcome. "Vanity Fair," "Pendennis" and "Henry Esmond" stand in the foremost rank of English fiction. Thackeray was a successful lecturer. His "English Humorists" and "The Four Georges," delivered before audiences in both England and America, added alike to his fame and his income.

THE WELCOME TO WALCOTE

(From "The History of Henry Esmond")

AS they came up to the house at Walcote, the windows from within were lighted up with friendly welcome; the supper-table was spread in the oak parlor; it seemed as if forgiveness and love were awaiting the returning prodigal. Two or three familiar faces of domestics were on the lookout at the porch—the old housekeeper was there, and young Lockwood from Castlewood in my lord's livery of tawny and blue. His dear mistress pressed his arm as they passed into the hall. Her eyes beamed out on him with affection indescribable. "Welcome," was all she said, as she looked up, putting back her fair curls and black hood. A sweet, rosy smile blushed on her face; Harry thought he had never seen her look so charming. Her face was lighted with a joy that was brighter than beauty—she took a hand of her son who was in the hall waiting his mother—she did not quit Esmond's arm.

"Welcome, Harry!" my young lord echoed after her. "Here we are all come to say so. Here's old Pincot, hasn't she grown handsome?" and Pincot, who was older and no handsomer than usual, made a courtesy to the Captain, as she called Esmond, and told my lord to "Have done now."

"And here's Jack Lockwood. He'll make a famous grenadier, Jack; and so shall I: we'll both 'list under you, cousin. As soon as I am seventeen I go to the army—every gentleman goes to the army. Look! who comes here—ho, ho!" he burst into a laugh. "'Tis Mistress 'Trix, with a new ribbon; I knew she would put one on as soon as she heard a Captain was coming to supper."

This laughing colloquy took place in the hall of Walcote House, in the midst of which is a staircase that leads from an open gallery where are the doors of the sleeping-chambers; and from one of these a wax candle in her hand, and illuminating her, came Mistress Beatrix—the light falling indeed upon the scarlet ribbon which she wore, and upon the most brilliant white neck in the world.

Esmond had left a child and found a woman, grown beyond the common height, and arrived at such a dazzling completeness of beauty that his eyes might well show surprise and delight at beholding her. In hers there was a brightness so lustrous and melting that I have seen a whole assembly follow her as if by an attraction irresistible; and that night

179

the great Duke was at the playhouse after Ramillies, every soul turned and looked (she chanced to enter at the opposite side of the theater at the same moment) at her, and not at him. She was a brown beauty —that is, her eyes, hair and eyebrows and eyelashes were dark; her hair curling with rich undulations, and waving over her shoulders. But her complexion was as dazzling white as snow in sunshine; except her cheeks, which were a bright red, and her lips, which were of a still deeper crimson. Her mouth and chin, they said, were too large and full, and so they might be for a goddess in marble, but not for a woman whose eyes were fire, whose look was love, whose voice was the sweetest low song, whose shape was perfect symmetry, health, decision, activity, whose foot, as it planted itself on the ground, was firm but flexible, and whose motion, whether rapid or slow, was always perfect grace—agile as a nymph, lofty as a queen—now melting, now imperious, now sarcastic—there was no single movement of hers but was beautiful. As he thinks of her, he who writes feels young again, and remembers a paragon.

So she came, holding her dress with one fair rounded arm, and her taper before her, tripping down the stairs to greet Esmond.

"She hath put on her scarlet stockings and white shoes," says my lord, still laughing. "Oh, my fine mistress! is this the way you set your cap at the Captain?" She approached, shining smiles upon Esmond, who could look at nothing but her eyes. She advanced, holding forward her head, as if she would have him kiss her as he used to do when she was a child.

"Stop," she said. "I am grown too big! Welcome, cousin Harry!" and she made him an arch courtesy, sweeping down to the ground almost, with the most gracious bend, looking up the while with the brightest eyes and sweetest smile. Love seemed to radiate from her. Harry eyed her with such a rapture as the first lover is described as having by Milton.

"N'est ce pas?" says my lady, in a low, sweet voice, still hanging on his arm.

Esmond turned round with a start and a blush, as he met his mistress's clear eyes. He had forgotten her, wrapped in admiration of the *filia pulcrior*.

"Right foot forward, toe turned out, so; now drop the courtesy, and show the red stockings, 'Trix. They've silver clocks, Harry. The Dowager sent 'em. She went to put 'em on," cries my lord.

"Hush, you stupid child!" says Miss, smothering her brother with kisses; and then she must come and kiss her mamma looking all the while at Harry, over his mistress's shoulder. And if she did not kiss him, she gave him both her hands, and then took one of his in both hands, and said, "Oh, Harry, we're *so* glad you're come!"

"There are woodcocks for supper," says my lord. "Huzza! it was such a hungry sermon."

"And it is the 29th of December, and our Harry has come home."

"Huzza, old Pincot!" again says my lord; and my dear lady's lips looked as if they were trembling with a prayer. She would have Harry lead in Beatrix to the supper-room, going herself with my young Lord Viscount; and to this party came Tom Tusher directly, whom four at least out of the company of five wished away. Away he went, however, as soon as the sweetmeats were put down; and then, by the great crackling fire, his mistress or Beatrix, with her blushing graces, filling his glass for him, Harry told the story of his campaign, and passed the most delightful night his life had ever known. The sun was up long ere he was, so deep, sweet, and refreshing was his slumber. He woke as if angels had been watching at his bed all night; I dare say one that was as pure and loving as an angel had blessed his sleep with her prayers.

Next morning the chaplain read prayers to the little household at Walcote, as the custom was; Esmond thought Mistress Beatrix did not listen to Tusher's exhortation much; her eyes were wandering everywhere during the service—at least whenever he looked up he met them. Perhaps he also was not very attentive to his reverence the chaplain. "This might have been my life," he was thinking; "this might have been my duty from now till old age. Well, were it not a pleasant one to be with these dear friends and part from 'em no more? Until—the destined lover comes and takes away pretty Beatrix"—and the best part of Tom Tusher's exposition, which may have been very learned and eloquent, was quite lost to poor Harry by this vision of the destined lover, who put the preacher out.

All the while of the prayers, Beatrix knelt a little way before Harry Esmond. The red stockings were changed for a pair of gray, and black shoes, in which her feet looked to the full as pretty. All the roses of spring could not vie with the brightness of her complexion; Esmond thought he had never seen anything like the sunny luster of her eyes. My Lady Viscountess looked fatigued, as if with watching, and her face was pale.

Miss Beatrix remarked these signs of indisposition in her mother, and deplored them. "I am an old woman," says my lady, with a kind smile; "I cannot hope to look as young as you do, my dear."

"She'll never look as good as you do if she lives till she's a hundred," says my lord, taking his mother by the waist, and kissing her hand.

"Do I look very wicked, cousin?" says Beatrix, turning full round on Esmond, with her pretty face so close under his chin that the soft, perfumed hair touched it. She laid her finger-tips on his sleeve as she spoke; and he put his other hand over hers.

"I'm like your looking-glass," says he, "and that can't flatter you."

"He means that you are always looking at him, my dear," says her mother, archly. Beatrix ran away from Esmond at this, and flew to her mamma, whom she kissed, stopping my lady's mouth with her pretty hand.

"And Harry is very good to look at," says my lady, with her fond eyes regarding the young man.

"If 'tis good to see a happy face," says he, "you see that." My lady said "Amen," with a sigh; and Henry thought the memory of her dead lord rose up and rebuked her back again into sadness; for her face lost the smile, and resumed its look of melancholy.

"Why, Harry, how fine we look in our scarlet and silver, and our black periwig!" cries my lord. "Mother, I am tired of my own hair. When shall I have a peruke? Where did you get your steenkirk, Harry?"

"It's some of my Lady Dowager's lace," says Harry: "she gave me this and a number of other fine things."

"My Lady Dowager isn't such a bad woman," my Lord continued.

"She's not so—so red as she is painted," says Miss Beatrix.

Her brother broke into a laugh. "I'll tell her you said so; by the Lord, 'Trix, I will!" he cries out.

"She'll know that you hadn't the wit to say it, my lord," says Miss Beatrix.

"We won't quarrel the first day Harry's here, will we, mother?" said the young lord. "We'll see if we can get on to the new year without a fight. Have some of this Christmas pie? and here comes the tankard; no, it's Pincot, with the tea."

"Will the Captain choose a dish?" asked Mistress Beatrix.

"I say, Harry," my lord goes on, "I'll show thee my horses after breakfast; and we'll go a-bird-netting to-night; and on Monday there's a cock-match at Winchester—do you love cock-fighting, Harry?—between the gentlemen of Sussex and the gentlemen of Hampshire, at ten pounds the battle, and fifty pounds the odd battle, to show one-and-twenty cocks."

"And what will you do, Beatrix, to amuse our kinsman?" asks my lady.

"I'll listen to him," says Beatrix; "I am sure he has a hundred things to tell us. And I'm jealous already of the Spanish ladies. Was that a beautiful nun at Cadiz, that you rescued from the soldiers? Your man talked of it last night in the kitchen, and Mrs. Betty told me this morning as she combed my hair. And he says you must be in love; for you sat on deck all night, and scribbled verses all day in your table-book."

Harry thought if he had wanted a subject for verses yesterday, to-day he had found one; and not all the Lindamiras and Ardelias of the poets were half so beautiful as this young creature, but he did not say so, though some one did for him.

This was his dear lady, who, after the meal was over, and the young people were gone, began talking of her children with Mr. Esmond, and of the characters of one and the other, and of her hopes and fears for both of them. "'Tis not while they are at home," she said, "and in their mother's nest I fear for them—'tis when they are gone into the world, whither I shall not be able to follow them. Beatrix will begin her service next year. You may have hard a rumor about—about my Lord Blandford. They were both children; and it is but idle talk. I know my kinswoman would never let him make such a poor marriage as our Beatrix would be. There's scarce a princess in Europe that she thinks is good enough for him or his ambition."

"There's not a princess in Europe to compare with her," says Esmond.

"In beauty? No, perhaps not," answered my lady. "She is most beautiful, isn't she? 'Tis not a mother's partiality that deceives me. I marked you yesterday when she came down the stair; and read it in your face. We look when you don't fancy us looking, and see better than you think, dear Harry; and just now when they spoke about your poems— you wrote pretty lines when you were but a boy—you thought Beatrix was a pretty subject for verse, did not you, Harry?" (The gentleman could only blush for a reply.) "And so she is; now are you the first that her pretty face has captivated. 'Tis quickly done. Such a pair of bright eyes as hers learn their power very soon, and use it very early." And looking at him keenly with hers, the fair widow left him.

And so it is—a pair of bright eyes with a dozen glances suffice to subdue a man; to enslave him and inflame him; to make him even forget; they dazzle him so that the past becomes straightway dim to him: and so he prizes them that he would give all his life to posses them. What is the fond love of dearest friends compared to this treasure? Is memory as strong as expectancy? fruition, as hunger? gratitude, as desire? I have looked at royal diamonds in the jewel-rooms in Europe, and thought how wars had been made about them. Mogul sovereigns deposed and strangled for them, or ransomed with them; millions expended to buy them; and daring lives lost in digging out the little shining toys that I value no more than the button in my hat. And so there are other glittering baubles, of rare water, too, for which men have been set to kill and quarrel ever since mankind began; and which last but for a score of years, when their sparkle is over. Where are those jewels now that beamed under Cleopatra's forehead, or shone in the sockets of Helen?

The second day after Esmond's coming to Walcote, Tom Tusher had leave to take a holiday, and went off in his very best gown and bands, to court the young woman whom his reverence desired to marry, and who was not a viscount's widow, as it turned out, but a brewer's relict, at Southampton, with a couple of thousand pounds to her fortune; for honest Tom's heart was under such excellent control that Venus herself, without a portion, would never have caused it to flutter. So he rode away on his heavy-paced gelding to pursue his jog-trot loves, leaving Esmond to the society of his dear mistress and her daughter, and with his young lord for a companion, who was charmed not only to see an old friend, but to have the tutor and his Latin books put out of the way.

The boy talked of things and people, and not a little about himself, in his frank, artless way. 'Twas easy to see that he and his sister had the better of their fond mother, for the first place in whose affections, though they fought constantly, and though the kind lady persisted that she loved both equally, 'twas not difficult to understand that Frank was his mother's darling and favorite. He ruled the whole household, always excepting rebellious Beatrix, not less now than when he was a child, marshaling the village boys in playing at soldiers, and caning them lustily, too, like the sturdiest corporal. As for Tom Tusher, his reverence treated the young lord with that politeness and deference which he always showed for a great man, whatever his age or stature was. Indeed, with respect to this young one, it was impossible not to love him, so frank and winning were his manners, his beauty, his gayety, the ring of

186

his laughter, and the delighted tone of his voice. Wherever he went he charmed and domineered. I think his old grandfather, the Dean, and the grim old housekeeper, Mrs. Pincot, were as much his slaves as his mother was; and as for Esmond, he found himself presently submitting to a certain fascination the boy had, and slaving it like the rest of the family. The pleasure which he had in Frank's mere company and converse exceeded that which he ever enjoyed in the society of any other man, however delightful in talk or famous for wit. His presence brought sunshine into a room, his laugh, his prattle, his noble beauty and brightness of look cheered and charmed indescribably. At the least tale of sorrow, his hands were in his purse, and he was eager with sympathy and bounty. The way in which women loved and petted him, when, a year or two afterward, he came upon the world, yet a mere boy, and the follies which they did for him (as indeed he for them), recalled the career of Rochester, and outdid the successes of Grammont. His very creditors loved him; and the hardest usurers, and some of the rigid prudes of the other sex, too, could deny him nothing. He was no more witty than another man, but what he said, he said and looked as no man else could say or look it. I have seen the women at the comedy at Bruxelles crowd round him in the lobby: and as he sat on the stage, more people looked at him than at the actors, and watched him; and I remember at Ramillies, when he was hit and fell, a great big red-haired Scotch sergeant flung his halberd down, burst out a-crying like a woman, seizing him up as if he had been an infant, and carrying him out of the fire. This brother and sister were the most beautiful couple ever seen; though after he winged away from the maternal nest, this pair were seldom together.

Sitting at dinner two days after Esmond's arrival

(it was the last day of the year), and so happy a one to Harry Esmond that to enjoy it was quite worth all the previous pain which he had endured and forgot, my young lord filling a bumper, and bidding Harry take another, drank to his sister, saluting her under the title of "Marchioness."

"Marchioness?" says Harry, not without a pang of wonder, for he was curious and jealous already.

"Nonsense, my lord," says Beatrix, with a toss of her head. My Lady Viscountess looked for a moment at Esmond, and cast her eyes down.

"The Marchioness of Blandford," says Frank. "Don't you know—hath not Rouge Dragon told you?" (My lord used to call the Dowager at Chelsea by this and other names.) "Blandford has a lock of her hair: the Duchess found him on his knees to Mistress Beatrix, and boxed his ears, and said Dr. Hare should whip him."

"I wish Mr. Tusher would whip you, too," said Beatrix.

My lady only said: "I hope you will tell none of these silly stories elsewhere than at home, Francis."

"'Tis true, on my word," continues Frank: "look at Harry scowling, mother, and see how Beatrix blushes as red as the silver-clocked stockings."

"I think we had best leave the gentlemen to their wine and their talk," says Mistress Beatrix, rising up with the air of a young queen, tossing her rustling, flowing draperies about her, and quitting the room, followed her mother.

Lady Castlewood again looked at Esmond, as she stooped down and kissed Frank. "Do not tell those silly stories, child," she said; "do not drink much wine, sir; Harry never loved to drink wine." And she went away, too, in her black robes, looking back on the young man with her fond, fair face.

"Egad! it's true," says Frank, sipping his wine,

with the air of a lord. "What think you of this Lisbon—real Collares? 'Tis better than your heady port; we got it out of one of the Spanish ships that came from Vigo last year; my mother bought it at Southampton, as the ship was lying there—the 'Rose,' Captain Hawkins."

"Why, I came home in that ship," says Harry.

"And it brought home a good fellow and good wine," says my lord. "I say, Harry, I wish thou hadst not that cursed bar sinister."

"And why not the bar sinister?" asks the other.

"Suppose I go to the army and am killed—every gentleman goes to the army—who is to take care of the women? 'Trix will never stop at home; mother's in love with you—yes, I think mother's in love with you. She was always praising you, and always talking about you; and when she went to Southampton to see the ship, I found her out. But you see it is impossible; we are of the oldest blood in England; we came in with the Conqueror; we were only baronets—but what then? we were forced into that. James the First forced our great-grandfather. We are above titles; we old English gentry don't want 'em. The Queen can make a duke any day. Look at Blandford's father, Duke Churchill, and Duchess Jennings, what were they, Harry? D—— it, sir, what are they, to turn up their noses at us? Where were they when our ancestors rode with King Henry at Agincourt, and filled up the French king's cup at Poictiers? 'Fore George, sir, why shouldn't Blandford marry Beatrix? By G——! he *shall* marry Beatrix, or tell me the reason why. We'll marry with the best blood of England, and none but the best blood of England. You are an Esmond, and can't help your birth, my boy. Let's have another bottle. What! no more? I've drunk three parts of this myself. I had many a night with my father. You stood to him like a man, Harry. You backed your blood; you can't help your misfortune, ~~you~~ know—no man can help that."

The elder said he would go into his mistress's tea-tabie. The young lad, with a heightened color and voice, began singing a snatch of a song, and marched out of the room. Esmond heard him presently calling his dogs about him, and cheering and talking to them; and by a hundred of his looks and gestures, tricks of voice and gait, was reminded of the dead lord, Frank's father.

And so the sylvester night passed away: the family parted long before midnight, Lady Castlewood remembering, no doubt, former New Years' eves, when healths were drunk, and laughter went round in the company of him, to whom years, past, present and future, were to be as one; and so cared not to sit with her children and hear the Cathedral bells ringing the birth of the year 1703. Esmond heard the chimes as he sat in his own chamber, ruminating by the blazing fire there, and listened to the last notes of them, looking out from his window toward the city, and the great gray towers of the Cathedral lying under the frosty sky, with the keen stars shining above.

The sight of these brilliant orbs no doubt made him think of other luminaries. "And so her eyes have already done execution," thought Esmond. "On whom?—who can tell me?"

THE DEATH OF COL. NEWCOME

From ("The Newcomes")

CLIVE, and the boy sometimes with him, used to go daily to Greyfriars, where the Colonel still lay ill. After some days the fever which had attacked him left him; but left him so weak and enfeebled that he could only go from his bed to

the chair by his fireside. The season was exceedingly
bitter, the chamber which he inhabited was warm
and spacious; it was considered unadvisable to move
him until he had attained greater strength, and till
warmer weather. The medical men of the House
hoped he might rally in spring. My friend, Dr.
Goodenough, came to him; he hoped too; but not
with a hopeful face. A chamber, luckily vacant,
hard by the Colonel's, was assigned to his friends,
where we sat when we were too many for him. Besides his customary attendant, he had two dear and
watchful nurses, who were almost always with him,
—Ethel and Madame de Florac, who had passed
many a faithful year by an old man's bedside; who
would have come, as to a work of religion, to any
sick couch, much more to this one, where he lay
for whose life she would once gladly have given her
own.

But our Colonel, we all were obliged to acknowledge, was no more our friend of old days. He knew
us again, and was good to every one round him, as
his wont was; especially when Boy came, his eyes
lighted up with simple happiness, and, with eager
trembling hands, he would seek under his bed-clothes,
or the pockets of his dressing-gown, for toys or
cakes which he had caused to be purchased for his
grandson. There was a little laughing, red-cheeked,
white-headed gown-boy of the school to whom the
old man had taken a great fancy. One of the
symptoms of his returning consciousness and recov-
ery, as we hoped, was his calling for this child, who
pleased our friend by his archness and merry ways;
and who, to the old gentleman's unfailing delight,
used to call him, "Codd Colonel." "Tell little
F——, that Codd Colonel wants to see him"; and the
little gown-boy was brought to him; and the Colonel
would listen to him for hours; and hear all about
his lessons and his play; and prattle almost as child-

ishly, about Doctor Raine, and his own early school-
days. The boys of the school, it must be said, had
heard the noble old gentleman's touching history,
and had all got to know and love him. They came
every day to hear news of him; sent him in books
and papers to amuse him; and some benevolent
young souls—God's blessing on all honest boys, say
I—painted theatrical characters, and sent them in
to Codd Colonel's grandson. The little fellow was
made free of gown-boys, and once came thence to
his grandfather in a little gown, which delighted the
old man hugely. Boy said he would like to be a
little gown-boy; and I make no doubt, when he is
old enough, his father will get him that post, and
put him under the tuition of my friend Dr. Senior.

So weeks passed away, during which our dear
old friend still remained with us. His mind was
gone at intervals, but would rally feebly; and with
his consciousness returned his love, his simplicity, his
sweetness. He would talk French with Madame de
Florac, at which time his memory appeared to
awaken with surprising vividness, his cheek flushed,
and he was a youth again,—a youth all love and
hope,—a stricken old man, with a beard as white as
snow covering the noble careworn face. At such
times he called her by her Christian name of
Léonore; he addressed courtly old words of regard
and kindness to the aged lady; anon he wandered in
his talk, and spoke to her as if they still were
young. Now, as in those early days, his heart was
pure; no anger remained in it; no guile tainted it;
only peace and good-will dwelt in it.

Rosey's death had seemed to shock him for a while
when the unconscious little boy spoke of it. Before
that circumstance Clive had even forborne to wear
mourning, lest the news should agitate his father.
The Colonel remained silent and was very much disturbed all that day, but he never appeared to com-

rehend the fact quite; and, once or twice afterwards, asked, Why she did not come to see him?
he was prevented, he supposed,—she was prevented,
he said, with a look of terror; he never once otherwise alluded to that unlucky tyrant of his household,
who had made his last years so unhappy.

The circumstance of Clive's legacy he never understood: but more than once spoke of Barnes to Ethel,
and sent his compliments to him, and said he should
like to shake him by the hand. Barnes Newcome
never once offered to touch that honored hand,
though his sister bore her uncle's message to him.
They came often from Bryanstone Square; Mrs.
Hobson even offered to sit with the Colonel, and
read to him, and brought him books for his improve-
ment. But her presence disturbed him; he cared
not for her books; the two nurses whom he loved
faithfully watched him; and my wife and I were
admitted to him sometimes, both of whom he honored wiht regard and recognition. As for F. B., in
order to be near his Colonel, did not that good fellow
take up his lodging in Cistercian Lane, at the "Red
Cow?" He is one whose errors, let us hope, shall
be pardoned, *quia multum amavit.* I am sure he
felt ten times more joy at hearing of Clive's legacy
than if thousands had been bequeathed to himself.
May good health and good fortune speed him!

The days went on, and our hopes, raised sometimes, began to flicker and fail. One evening the
Colonel left his chair for his bed in pretty good
spirits, but passed a disturbed night, and the next
morning was too weak to rise. Then he remained in
his bed, and his friends visited him there. One
afternoon he asked for his little gown-boy, and the
child was brought to him, and sat by the bed with
a very awe-stricken face; and then gathered courage,
and tried to amuse him by telling him how it was a
half-holiday, and they were having a cricket match

with the St. Peter's boys in the green, and Greyfriars was in and winning. The Colonel quite understood about it; he would like to see the game; he had played many a game on that green when he was a boy. He grew excited; Clive dismissed his father's little friend, and put a sovereign into his hand; and away he ran to say that Codd Colonel had come into a fortune, and to buy tarts, and to see the match out. *I, curre,* little white-haired gown-boy! Heaven speed you, little friend.

After the child had gone, Thomas Newcome began to wander more and more. He talked louder; he gave the word of command, spoke Hindustanee as if to his men. Then he spoke words in French rapidly, seizing a hand that was near him, and crying, "Toujours, toujours!" But it was Ethel's hand which he took. Ethel and Clive and the nurse were in the room with him; the nurse came to us, who were sitting in the adjoining apartment; Madame de Florac was there, with my wife and Bayham.

At the look in the woman's countenance Madame de Florac started up. "He is very bad, he wanders a great deal," the nurse whispered. The French lady fell instantly on her knees, and remained rigid in prayer.

Some time afterwards Ethel came in with a scared face to our pale group. "He is calling for you again, dear lady," she said, going up to Madame de Florac, who was still kneeling; "and just now he said he wanted Pendennis to take care of his boy. He will not know you." She hid her tears as she spoke.

She went into the room where Clive was at the bed's foot; the old man within it talked on rapidly for a while: then again he would sigh and be still: once more I heard him say hurriedly, "Take care of him when I'm in India"; and then with a heart-rending voice he called out, "Léonore, Léonore!"

She was kneeling by his side now. The patient's voice sank into faint murmurs; only a moan now and then announced that he was not asleep.

At the usual evening hour the chapel bell began to toll, and Thomas Newcome's hands outside the bed feebly beat a time. And just as the last bell struck, a peculiar sweet smile shone over his face, and he lifted up his head a little, and quickly said, " Adsum!" and fell back. It was the word we used at school, when names were called; and lo, he, whose heart was as that of a little child, had answered to his name, and stood in the presence of The Master.

BECKY IN LUCK

(From "Vanity Fair")

AT last Becky's kindness and attention to the chief of her husband's family were destined to meet with an exceeding great reward; a reward which, though certainly somewhat unsubstantial, the little woman coveted with greater eagerness than more positive benefits. If she did not wish to lead a virtuous life, at least she desired to enjoy a character for virtue, and we know that no lady in the genteel world can possess this desideratum, until she has put on a train and feathers, and has been presented to her sovereign at court. From that august interview they come out stamped as honest women. The lord chamberlain gives them a certificate of virtue. And as dubious goods or letters are passed through an oven at quarantine, sprinkled with aromatic vinegar, and then pronounced clean—many a lady whose reputation would be doubtful otherwise, and liable to give infection, passes through the wholesome ordeal of the royal presence, and issues from it free from all taint.

It might be very well for my Lady Bareacres, my Lady Tufto, Mrs. Bute Crawley in the country,

and other ladies who had come into contact with
Mrs. Rawdon Crawley, to cry fie at the idea of
the odious little adventuress making her courtesy
before the sovereign; and to declare that, if dear,
good Queen Charlotte had been alive, *she* never
would have admitted such an extremely ill-regulated
personage into her chaste drawing-room. But when
we consider that it was the First Gentleman in
Europe in whose high presence Mrs. Rawdon passed
her examination, and, as it were, took her degree
in reputation, it surely must be flat disloyalty to
doubt any more about her virtue. I, for my part,
look back with love and awe to that Great Character in history. Ah, what a high and noble appreciation of Gentlewomanhood there must have been
in Vanity Fair, when that revered and august being
was invested, by the universal acclaim of the re-
fined and educated portion of this empire, with the
title of Premier Gentilhomme of his Kingdom! Do
you remember, dear M———, O friend of my youth,
how one blissful night five-and-twenty years since,
the "Hypocrite" being acted, Elliston being manager, Dowton and Liston performers, two boys had
leave from their loyal masters to go out from
Slaughter House School, where they were educated
and to appear on Drury Lane stage, amongst a
crowd which assembled there to greet the king.
THE KING! There he was. Beef-eaters were before the august box, the Marquis of Steyne (Lord of
the Powder Closet), and other great officers of state
were behind the chair on which he sat, *He* sat—
florid of face, portly of person, covered with orders,
and in a rich curling head of hair. How we sang
God save him! How the house rocked and shouted
with that magnificent music. How they cheered
and cried, and waved handerchiefs. Ladies wept
mothers clasped their children: some fainted with
emotion. People were suffocated in the pit, shriek

and groans rising up amidst the writhing and shout-- ing mass there of his people who were, and indeed showed themselves almost to be, ready to die for him. Yes, we saw him. Fate cannot deprive us of *that*. Others have seen Napoleon. Some few still exist who have beheld Frederick the Great, Dr. Johnson, Marie Antoinette, etc.—be it our reasonable boast to our children, that we saw George the Good, the Magnificent, the Great.

Well, there came a happy day in Mrs. Rawdon Crawley's existence, when this angel was admitted into the paradise of a Court which she coveted; her sister-in-law acting as her godmother. On the appointed day, Sir Pitt and his lady, in their great family carriage (just newly built, and ready for the baronet's assumption of the office of High Sheriff of his county), drove up to the little house in Curzon Street; to the edification of Raggles, who was watching from his green-grocer's shop, and saw fine plumes within, and enormous bunches of flowers in the breasts of the new livery-coats of the footmen.

Sir Pitt, in a glittering uniform, descended and went into Curzon Street, his sword between his legs. Little Rawdon stood with his face against the parlor window-panes, smiling and nodding with all his might to his aunt in the carriage within; and presently Sir Pitt issued forth from the house again, leading forth a lady with grand feathers, covered in a white shawl, and holding up daintily a train of magnificent brocade. She stepped into the vehicle as if she were a princess, and accustomed all her life to go to Court, smiling graciously on the footman at the door, and on Sir Pitt, who followed her into the carriage.

Then Rawdon followed in his old Guards uniform, which had grown woefully shabby, and was much too tight. He was to have followed the procession, and waited upon his sovereign in a cab, but that his good-natured sister-in-law insisted that they should be a family party. The coach was large, the ladies not very big—they would hold their trains in their laps. Finally, the four went fraternally together, and their carriage presently joined the line of loyal equipages which was making its way down Piccadilly and St. James's Street, toward the old brick palace, where the Star of Brunswick was in waiting to receive his nobles and gentle-folks.

Becky felt as if she could bless the people out of the carriage windows, so elated was she in spirit, and so strong a sense had she of the dignified position which she had at last attained in life. Even our Becky had her weaknesses, and as one often sees how men pride themselves upon excellences which others are slow to perceive: how, for instance, Comus firmly believes that he is the greatest tragic actor in England, how Brown, the famous novelist, longs to be considered, not a man of genuis, but a man of fashion; while Robinson, the great lawyer, does not in the least care about his reputation in Westminster Hall, but believes himself incompara-ble across country, and at a five-barred gate—so to be, and to be thought, a respectable woman, was Becky's aim in life, and she got up the genteel with amazing assiduity, readiness and success. We have said, there were times when she believed her-self to be a fine lady, and forgot that there was no money in the chest at home—duns round the gate, tradesmen to coax and wheedle—no ground to walk upon, in a word. And as she went to court in the carriage, the family carriage, she adopted a de-meanor so grand, self-satisfied, deliberate and im-posing, that it made even Lady Jane laugh. She walked into the royal apartments with a toss of the head which would have befitted an empress, and have no doubt, had she been one, she would have become the character perfectly.

We are authorized to state that Mrs. Rawdon Crawley's *costume de cour* on the occasion of her presentation to the sovereign was of the most elegant and brilliant description. Some ladies we may have seen—we who wear stars and cordons, and attend the St. James's assemblies, or we who, in muddy boots, dawdle up and down Pall Mall, and peep into the coaches as they drive up with the great folks in their feathers—some ladies of fashion, I say, we may have seen, about two o'clock of the forenoon of a levee day, as the laced-jacketed band of the Life Guards are blowing triumphal marches seated on those prancing music-stools, their cream-colored chargers—who are by no means lovely and enticing objects at that early period of noon. A stout countess of sixty, *décolletée,* painted, wrinkled, with rouge up to her drooping eyelids, and diamonds twinkling in her wig, is a wholesome and edifying, but not a pleasant sight. She has the faded look of a St. James's Street illumination, as it may be seen of an early morning, when half the lamps are out, and the others are blinking wanly, as if they were about to vanish like ghosts before the dawn. Such charms as those of which we catch glimpses while her ladyship's carriage passes should appear abroad at night alone. If even Cynthia looks haggard of an afternoon, as we may see her sometimes in the present winter season, with Phœbus staring her out of countenance from the opposite side of the heavens, how much more can old Lady Castlemouldy keep her head up when the sun is shining full upon it through the chariot windows, and showing all the chinks and crannies with which time hâs marked her face? No. Drawing-rooms should be announced for November, or the first foggy day: or the elderly sultanas of our Vanity

Fair should drive up in closed litters, descend in a covered way, and make their courtesy to the sovereign under the protection of lamplight.

Our beloved Rebecca had no need, however, of any such a friendly halo to set off her beauty. Her complexion could bear any sunshine as yet; and her dress, though, if you were to see it now, any present lady of Vanity Fair would pronounce it to be the most foolish and preposterous attire ever worn, was as handsome in her eyes and those of the public, some five-and-twenty years since, as the most brilliant costume of the most famous beauty of the present season. A score of years hence that, too, that milliner's wonder, will have passed into the domain of the absurd, along with all previous vanities. But we are wandering too much. Mrs. Rawdon's dress was pronounced to be *charmante* on the eventful day of her presentation. Even good little Lady Jane was forced to acknowledge this effect, as she looked at her kinswoman; and owned sorrowfully to herself that she was quite inferior in taste to Mrs. Becky.

She did not know how much care, throught, and genius Mrs. Rawdon had bestowed upon that garment. Rebecca had as good taste as any milliner in Europe, and such a clever way of doing things as Lady Jane little understood. The latter quickly spied out the magnificence of the brocade of Becky's train, and the splendor of the lace on her dress.

The brocade was an old remnant, Becky said; and as for the lace, it was a great bargain. She had had it these hundred years.

"My dear Mrs. Crawley, it must have cost a little fortune," Lady Jane said, looking down at her own lace, which was not nearly so good; and then, examining the quality of the ancient brocade which formed the material of Mrs. Rawdon's court dress, she felt inclined to say that she could not afford such fine clothing, but checked that speech, with an effort, as one uncharitable to her kinswoman.

And yet, if Lady Jane had known all, I think even her kindly temper would have failed her. The fact is, when she was putting Sir Pitt's house in order, Mrs. Rawdon had found the lace and the brocade in old wardrobes, the property of the former ladies of the house, and had quietly carried the goods home, and had suited them to her own little person. Briggs saw her take them, asked no questions, told no stories; but I believe quite sympathized with her on this matter, and so would many another honest woman.

And the diamonds—"Where the doose did you get the diamonds, Becky?" said her husband, admiring some jewels which he had never seen before, and which sparkled in her ears and on her neck with brilliance and profusion.

Becky blushed a little, and looked at him hard for a moment. Pitt Crawley blushed a little too, and looked out of the window. The fact is, he had given her a very small portion of the brilliants; a pretty diamond clasp, which confined a pearl necklace which she wore, and the baronet had omitted to mention the circumstance to his lady.

Becky looked at her husband, and then at Sir Pitt, with an air of saucy triumph—as much as to say: "Shall I betray you?"

"Guess!" she said to her husband. "Why, you silly man," she continued, "where do you suppose I got them?—all except this little clasp, which a dear friend of mine gave me long ago. I hired them, to be sure. I hired them at Mr. Polonius's, in Coventry Street. You don't suppose that all the diamonds which go to court belong to the owners; like those beautiful stones which Lady Jane has, and which are much handsomer than any which I have, I am certain."

"They are family jewels," said Sir Pitt, again looking uneasy. And in this family conversation the carriage rolled down the street, until its cargo was finally discharged at the gates of the palace where the sovereign was sitting in state.

The diamonds, which had created Rawdon's admiration, never went back to Mr. Polonius, of Coventry Street, and that gentleman never applied for their restoration; but they retired into a little private repository, in an old desk, which Amelia Sedley had given her years and years ago, and in which Becky kept a number of useful and, perhaps, valuable things, about which her husband knew nothing. To know nothing, or little, is in the nature of some husbands. To hide is the nature of how many women? O ladies! how many of you have surreptitious milliners' bills? How many of you have gowns and bracelets, which you daren't show, or which you wear trembling?—trembling, and coaxing with smiles the husband by your side, who does not know the new velvet gown from the old one, or the new bracelet from the last year's, or has any notion that the ragged-looking yellow lace scarf cost forty guineas, and that Madame Bobinot is writing dunning letters every week for the money!

Thus Rawdon knew nothing about the brilliant diamond earrings, or the superb brilliant ornament which decorated the fair bosom of his lady; but Lord Steyne, who was in his place at court, as Lord of the Powder Closet, and one of the great dignitaries and illustrious defences of the throne of England, and came up with all his stars, garters, collars, and cordons, and paid particular attention to the little woman, knew whence the jewels came, and who paid for them.

As he bowed over her he smiled, and quoted the hackneyed and beautiful lines from the "Rape of the Lock," about Belinda's diamonds, which Jews might kiss and infidels adore.

"But I hope your lordship is orthodox," said the little lady, with a toss of her head. And many ladies round about whispered and talked, and many gentlemen nodded and whispered, as they saw what marked attention the great nobleman was paying to the little adventuress.

What were the circumstances of the interview between Rebecca Crawley, née Sharp, and her Imperial Master, it does not become such a feeble and inexperienced pen as mine to attempt to relate. The dazzled eyes close before that Magnificent Idea. Loyal respect and decency tell even the imagination not to look too keenly and audaciously about the sacred audience-chamber, but to back away rapidly, silently, and respectfully, making profound bows out of the August Presence.

This may be said, that in all London there was no more loyal heart than Becky's after this interview. The name of her king was always on her lips, and he was proclaimed by her to be the most charming of men. She went to Colnaghi's and ordered the finest portrait of him that art had produced, and credit could supply. She chose that famous one in which the best of monarchs is represented in a frock-coat with a fur collar, and breeches and silk stockings, simpering on a sofa from under his curly brown wig. She had him painted in a brooch and wore it—indeed she amused and somewhat pestered her acquaintance with her perpetual talk about his urbanity and beauty. Who knows? Perhaps the little woman thought she might play the part of a Maintenon or a Pompadour.

But the finest sport of all after her presentation was to hear her talk virtuously. She had a few female acquaintances, not, it must be owned, of the very highest reputation in Vanity Fair. But being made an honest woman of, so to speak, Becky would not consort any longer with these dubious ones, and cut Lady Crackenbury when the latter nodded to her from her opera-box; and gave Mrs. Washington White the go-by in the Ring. "One must, my dear, show one is somebody," she said. "One mustn't be seen with doubtful people. I pity Lady Crackenbury from my heart: and Mrs. Washington White may be a very good-natured person. *You* may go and dine with them, as you like your rubber. But *I* mustn't, and won't; and you will have the goodness to tell Smith to say I am not at home when either of them calls."

The particulars of Becky's costume were in the newspapers—feathers, lappets, superb diamonds, and all the rest. Mrs. Crackenbury read the paragraph in bitterness of spirit, and discoursed to her followers about the airs which that woman was giving herself. Mrs. Bute Crawley and her young ladies in the country had a copy of the "Morning Post" from town; and gave a vent to their honest indignation. "If you had been sandy-haired, green-eyed, and a French rope-dancer's daughter," Mrs. Bute said to her eldest girl (who, on the contrary, was a very swarthy, short, and snub-nosed young lady), "you might have had superb diamonds forsooth, and have been presented at court by your cousin, the Lady Jane. But you're only a gentlewoman, my poor dear child. You have only some of the best blood in England in your veins, and good principles and piety for your portion. I, myself, the wife of a baronet's younger brother, too, never thought of such a thing as going to court—nor would other people, if good Queen Charlotte had been alive." In this way the worthy rectoress consoled herself; and her daughters sighed, and sat over the "Peerage" all night.

A few days after the famous presentation, another

great and exceeding honor was vouchsafed to the virtuous Becky. Lady Steyne's carriage drove up to Mr. Rawdon Crawley's door, and the footman, instead of driving down the front of the house, as by his tremedous knocking he appeared to be inclined to do, relented, and only delivered in a couple of cards on which were engraven the names of the Marchioness of Steyne and the Countess of Gaunt. If these bits of pasteboard had been beautiful pictures, or had had a hundred yards of Malines lace rolled round them, worth twice the number of guineas, Becky could not have regarded them with more pleasure. You may be sure they occupied a conspicuous place in the china bowl on the drawing-room table, where Becky kept the cards of her visitors. Lord! lord! how poor Mrs. Washington White's card and Lady Crackenbury's card, which our little friend had been glad enough to get a few months back, and of which the silly little creature was rather proud once—lord! lord! I say, how soon, at the appearance of these grand court cards, did those poor little neglected deuces sink down to the bottom of the pack. Steyne! Bareacres, Johnes of Helvellyn! and Caerlyon of Camelot! we may be sure that Becky and Briggs looked out those august names in the "Peerage," and followed the noble race up through all the ramifications of the family tree.

My Lord Steyne coming to call a couple of hours afterward, and looking about him, and observing everything as was his wont, found his lady's cards already ranged as the trumps of Becky's hand, and grinned, as this old cynic always did at any naïve display of human weakness. Becky came down to him presently; whenever the dear girl expected his lordship, her toilet was prepared, her hair in perfect order, her mouchoirs, aprons, scarfs, little morocco slippers, and other female gimcracks arranged, and she seated in some artless and agreeable posture ready to receive him—whenever she was surprised. Of course she had to fly to her apartment to take a rapid survey of matters in the glass, and to trip down again to wait upon the great peer.

She found him grinning over the bowl. She was discovered, and she blushed a little. "Thank you, monsigneur," she said. "You see your ladies have been here. How good of you! I couldn't come before—I was in the kitchen making a pudding."

"I know you were, I saw you through the area-railings as I drove up," replied the old gentleman.

"You see everything," she replied.

"A few things, but not that, my pretty lady," he said good-naturedly. "You silly little fibster! I heard you in the room overhead, where I have no doubt you were putting a little rouge on; you must give some of yours to my Lady Gaunt, whose complexion is quite preposterous; and I heard the bedroom door open, and then you came downstairs."

"Is it a crime to try and look my best when *you* come here?" answered Mrs. Rawdon plaintively, and she rubbed her cheek with her handerchief as if to show there was no rouge at all, only genuine blushes and modesty in her case. About this who could tell? I know there is some rouge that won't come off on a pocket-handkerchief, and some so good that even tears will not disturb it.

"Well," said the old gentleman, twiddling round his wife's card, "you are bent on becoming a fine lady. You pester my poor old life out to get you into the world. You won't be able to hold your own there, you silly little fool. You've got no money."

"You will get us a place," interposed Becky, as quick as possible.

"You've got no money, and you want to compete with those who have. You poor little earthenware pipkin, you want to swim down the stream along with the great copper kettles. All women are alike. Everybody is striving for what is not worth the having! I dined with the king yesterday, and we had neck of mutton and turnips. A dinner of herbs is better than a stalled ox very often. You will go to Gaunt House. You give an old fellow no rest until you get there. It's not half so nice as here. You'll be bored there. I am. My wife is as gay as Lady Macbeth, and my daughters as cheerful as Regan and Goneril. I daren't sleep in what they call my bedroom. The bed is like the baldaquin of St. Peter's and the pictures frighten me. I have a little brass bed in a dressing-room, and a little hair mattress like an anchorite. I am an anchorite. Ho, ho! You'll be asked to dinner next week. And *gare aux femmes,* look out and hold your own! How the women will bully you!" This was a very long speech for a man of few words like my Lord Steyne; nor was it the first which he uttered for Becky's benefit on that day.

Briggs looked up from the work at which she was seated in the further room, and gave a deep sigh as she heard the great marquis speak so lightly of her sex.

"If you don't turn off that abominable sheep-dog," said Lord Steyne, with a savage look over his shoulder at her, "I will have her poisoned."

"I always give my dog dinner from my own plate," said Rebecca, laughing mischievously; and having enjoyed for some time the discomfiture of my lord, who hated poor Briggs for interrupting his *tête-à-tête* with the fair colonel's wife, Mrs. Rawdon at length had pity upon her admirer, and calling to Briggs, praised the fineness of the weather to her, and bade her to take out the child for a walk.

"I can't send her away," Becky said presently,

after a pause, and in a very sad voice. Her eye
filled with tears as she spoke, and she turned away
her head.

"You owe her her wages, I suppose?" said the
peer.

"Worse than that," said Becky, still casting down
her eyes. "I have ruined her!"

"Ruined her?—then why don't you turn her out?"
the gentleman asked.

"Men do that," Becky answered, bitterly. "Wom
en are not so bad as you. Last year, when we
were reduced to our last guinea, she gave us every
thing. She shall never leave me until we are ruined
utterly ourselves, which does not seem far off, or
until I can pay her the utmost farthing."

"—— it, how much is it? asked the peer. And
Becky, reflecting on the largeness of his means,
mentioned not only the sum which she had borrowed
from Miss Briggs, but one of nearly double the
amount.

This caused the Lord Steyne to break out in
another brief and energetic expression of anger, at
which Rebecca held down her head the more, and
cried bitterly. "I could not help it. It was my
only chance. I dare not tell my husband. He
would kill me if I told him what I have done. I
have kept it a secret from everybody but you—and
you forced it from me. Ah, what shall I do, Lord
Steyne! for I am very, very unhappy."

Lord Steyne made no reply except by beating
the tattoo, and biting his nails. At last he
clapped his hat on his head, and flung out of the
room. Rebecca did not rise from her attitude of
misery until the door slammed upon him, and his
carriage whirled away. Then she rose up with the
queerest expression of victorious mischief glittering
in her green eyes. She burst out laughing once
or twice to herself, as she sat at work; and, sitting

down to the piano, she rattled away a triumphant voluntary on the keys, which made the people pause under her window to listen to her brilliant music.

That night, there came two notes from Gaunt House for the little woman, the one containing a card of invitation from Lord and Lady Steyne to a dinner at Gaunt House next Friday; while the other inclosed a slip of gray paper bearing Lord Steyne's signature and the address of Messrs. Jones, Brown & Robinson, Lombard street.

Rawdon heard Becky laughing in the night once or twice. It was only her delight at going to Gaunt House and facing the ladies there, she said, which amused her so. But the truth was, that she was occupied with a great number of other thoughts. Should she pay off old Briggs and give her her *congé?* Should she astonish Raggles by settling his account? She turned over all these thoughts on her pillow, and on the next day when Rawdon went out to pay his morning visit to the club, Mrs. Crawley (in a modest dress, with a veil on) whipped off in a hackney coach to the City; and, being landed at Messrs. Jones & Robinson's bank, presented a document there to the authority at the desk, who, in reply, asked her "How she would take it?"

She gently said "she would take a hundred and fifty pounds in small notes and the remainder in one note;" and passing through St. Paul's church-yard stopped there and bought the handsomest black silk gown for Briggs which money could buy; and which, with a kiss and the kindest speeches, she presented to the simple old spinster.

Then she walked to Mr. Raggles, inquired about his children affectionately, and gave him fifty pounds on account. Then she went to the liveryman from whom she jobbed her carriages, and gratified him with a similar sum. "And I hope this will be a lesson to you, Spavin," she said; "and that on the next drawing-room day my brother, Sir Pitt, will not be inconvenienced by being obliged to take four of us in his carriage to wait upon his majesty, because my own carriage is not forthcoming." It appears there had been a difference on the last drawing-room day. Hence the degradation which the colonel had almost suffered of being obliged to enter the presence of his sovereign in a hack-cab.

These arrangements concluded, Becky paid a visit upstairs to the before-mentioned desk, which Amelia Sedley had given her years and years ago, and which contained a number of useful and valuable little things: in which private museum she placed the one note which Messrs. Jones & Robinson's cashier had given her.

THE FOTHERINGAY OFF THE STAGE

(From "Pendennis")

AS Pen followed his companion up the creaking old stairs his knees trembled under him. He could hardly see when he entered, following the Captain, and stood in the room—in her room. He saw something black before him, and waving as if making a courtesy; and heard, but quite indistinctly, Costigan making a speech over him, in which the Captain, with his habitual magniloquence, expressed to "me child" his wish to make her known to "his dear and admirable young friend, Mr. Arthur Pindinnis, a young gentleman of property in the neighborhood, a person of refoined moind and amiable manners, a sincere lover of poethry; and a man possest of a feeling and affectionate heart."

"It is very fine weather," Miss Fotheringay said, in an Irish accent, and with a deep, rich, melancholy voice.

"Very," said Mr. Pendennis.

"And very warm," continued this Empress and Queen of Sheba.

In this romantic way the conversation began; and he found himself seated on a chair and having leisure to look at the young lady. She looked still handsomer off the stage than before the lamps. All her attitudes were naturally grand and majestic. If she went up and stood before the mantel-piece, her robe draped itself classically round her; her chin supported itself on her hand; the other lines of her form arranged themselves in full harmonious undulation. She looked like a muse in contemplation. If she sat down on a cane-bottomed chair, her arm rounded itself over the back of the seat; her hand seemed as if it ought to have a sceptre put into it; the folds of her dress fell naturally around her in order; all her movements were graceful and imperial.

The conversation thus begun rolled on. She asked Costigan whether he had had a pleasant evening at the George, and he recounted the supper and the tumblers of punch. Then the father asked her how she had been employed during the morning.

"Bows came," said she, "at ten, and we studied Ophaylia. It's for the twenty-fourth, when I hope, sir, we shall have the honor of seeing ye."

"Indeed you will," Mr. Pendennis cried: wondering she should say "Ophaylia," and speak with an Irish inflection of voice naturally, who had not the least Hibernian accent on the stage.

"I've secured 'um for your benefit, dear," said the Captain, tapping his waistcoat-pocket, wherein lay Pen's sovereigns, and winking at Pen with one eye, at which the boy blushed.

"Mr. —— the gentleman's very obleeging," said Mrs. Haller.

"My name is Pendennis," said Pen, blushing. "I—I—hope you'll—you'll remember it." His heart thumped so as he made this audacious declaration, that he almost choked in uttering it.

"Pendennis," she answered slowly, and looking him full in the eyes, with a glance so straight, so clear, so bright, so killing, with a voice so sweet, so round, so low, that the word transfixed him with pleasure.

"I never knew the name was so pretty before," Pen said.

"'Tis a very pretty name," Orphelia said. "Pentweazle's not a pretty name. Remember, papa, when we were on the Norwich circuit, young Pentweazle, who used to play second old man, and married Miss Raney, the Columbine? They're both engaged in London now, at the Queen's, and get five pounds a week. Pentweazle wasn't his real name. 'Twas Jedkin gave it him, I don't know why. His name was Harrington; that is, his real name was Potts; fawther a clergyman very respectable. Harrington was in London, and got into debt. Ye remember, he came out in Falkland, to Mrs. Bunce's Julia."

"And a pretty Julia she was," the Captain interposed; "a woman of fifty, and a mother of ten children. 'Tis you who ought to have been Julia, or my name's not Jack Costigan."

"I didn't take the leading business then," Miss Fotheringay said, modestly. "I wasn't fit for 't till Bows taught me."

"True for you, my dear," said the Captain; and bending to Pendennis, he added, "Rejuiced in circumstances, sir, I was for some time a fencing-master in Dublin; (there's only three men in the empire could touch me with the foil once, but Jack Costigan's getting old and stiff now, sir) and my daughter had an engagement at the thayater there; and 'twas there that my friend, Mr. Bows, gave her lessons, and made her what ye see. What have ye done since Bows went, Emily?"

"Sure, I've made a pie," Emily said, with perfect simplicity. She pronounced it *poy*.

"If ye'll try it at four o'clock, sir, say the word," said Costigan gallantly. "That girl, sir, makes the best veal and ham pie in England; and I think I can promise ye a glass of punch of the right flavor."

Pen had promised to be home at dinner at six o'clock; but the rascal thought he could accommodate pleasure and duty in this point, and was only too eager to accept this invitation. He looked on with wonder and delight whilst Ophelia busied herself about the room, and prepared for dinner. She arranged the glasses, and laid and smoothed the little cloth, all which duties she performed with a quiet grace and good-humor which enchanted her guest more and more. The "poy" arrived from the baker's at the proper hour; and at four o'clock Pen found himself at dinner—actually at dinner with the handsomest woman in creation—with his first and only love, whom he had adored ever since when? ever since yesterday, ever since forever.

Pen tried to engage her in conversation about poetry and about her profession. He asked her what she thought of Ophelia's madness, and whether she was in love with Hamlet or not. "In love with such a little ojus wretch as that stunted manager of a Bingley!" She bristled with indignation at the thought. Pen explained that it was not her of whom he spoke, but of the Ophelia of the play. "Oh, indeed, if no offence was meant, none was taken; but as for Bingley, indeed, she did not value him—not that glass of punch!"

Pen next tried her on Kotzebue. "Kotzebue? Who was he?" "The author of the play in which she had been performing so admirably." "She did not know that—the man's name at the beginning of the book was Thompson," said she. Pen laughed at her adorable simplicity. He told her of the melan-

213

choly fate of the author of the play, and how Sand
had killed him. It was the first time in her life
that Miss Costigan had ever heard of Mr. Kotzebue's
existence; but she looked as if she was very much
interested, and her sympathy sufficed for honest Pen.
In the midst of this conversation the hour and a
quarter which poor Pen could afford to allow himself passed away only too quickly; and he had taken
leave; he was gone, and away on his rapid road
homeward on the back of Rebecca. She was called
upon to show her mettle in the three journeys which
she made that day. . . .

"What was that he was talking about, the madness
of Hamlet, and the theory of the great German
critic on the subject?" Emily asked of her father.

"'Deed then, I don't know, Milly dear," answered
the Captain. "We'll ask Bows when he comes."

"Anyhow, he's a nice, fair-spoken, pretty young
man," the lady said. "How many tickets did he
take of you?"

"Faith, then, he took six, and gev me two guineas,
Milly," the Captain said. "I suppose them young
chaps is not too flush of coin."

"He's full of book-learning," Miss Fotheringay
continued. "Kotzebue! He, he, what a droll name,
indeed, now; and the poor fellow killed by sand,
too! Did ye ever hear such a thing? I'll ask Bows
about it, papa dear."

"A queer death, sure enough," ejaculated the
Captain, and changed the painful theme. "'Tis an
elegant mare the young gentleman rides," Costigan
went on to say, "and a grand breakfast intirely,
that young Mister Foker gave us."

"He's good for two private boxes, and at least
twenty tickets, I should say," cried the daughter.

"I'll go bail of that," answered the papa. And
so the conversation continued for a while, until the
tumbler of punch was finished; and their hour of

departure soon came, too; for at half-past six Miss Fotheringay was to appear at the theater again, whither her father always accompanied her.

"How beautiful she is," thought Pen, cantering homeward. "How simple and how tender! How charming it is to a see a woman of her genius busying herself with the humble offices of domestic life, cooking dishes to make her old father comfortable, and brewing him drink! How rude it was of me to begin to talk about professional matters, and how well she turned the conversation! By-the-way, she talked about professional matters herself; but then with what fun and humor she told the story of her comrade, Pentweazle, as he was called! There is no humor like Irish humor. Her father is rather tedious, but thoroughly amiable; and how fine of him giving lessons in fencing, after he quitted the army, where he was the pet of the Duke of Kent! Fencing! I should like to continue my fencing, or I shall forget what Angelo taught me. Uncle Arthur always liked me to fence; he says it is the exercise of a gentleman. Hang it! I'll take some lessons of Captain Costigan. Go along, Rebecca—up the hill, old lady! Pendennis, Pendennis—how she spoke the word! Emily, Emily! how good, how noble, how beautiful, how perfect she is!"

Now the reader, who has had the benefit of hearing the entire conversation which Pen had with Miss Fotheringay, can judge for himself about the powers of her mind, and may perhaps be disposed to think that she has not said anything astonishingly humorous or intellectual in the course of the *above* interview.

THE CANE-BOTTOMED CHAIR

IN tattered old slippers that toast at the bars,
  And a ragged old jacket perfumed with cigars,
Away from the world and its toils and its cares,
I've a snug little kingdom up four pair of stairs.

To mount to this realm is a toil, to be sure,
But the fire there is bright, and the air rather pure;
And the view I behold on a sunshiny day
Is grand through the chimney-pots over the way.

This snug little chamber is crammed in all nooks
With worthless old knick-knacks and silly old books,
And foolish old odds and foolish old ends,
Crooked bargains from brokers, cheap keepsakes
      from friends.

Old armor, prints, pictures, pipes, china (all cracked),
Old rickety tables, and chairs broken-backed,
A two-penny treasury, wondrous to see;
What matter? 'tis pleasant to you, friend, and me.

Long, long through the hours, and the night, and
      the chimes,
Here we talk of old books, and old friends, and old
      times;
As we sit in a fog made of rich Latakie
This chamber is pleasant to you, friend, and me.

But of all the cheap treasures that garnish my nest,
There's one that I love and I cherish the best:
For the finest of cochees that's padded with hair
I never would change thee, my cane-bottomed chair.

THE CANE-BOTTOMED CHAIR

'Tis a bandy-legged, high-shouldered, worm-eaten
     seat,
With a creaking old back and twisted old feet;
But since the fair morning when Fanny sat there,
I bless thee and love thee, old cane-bottomed chair.

If chairs have but feeling, in holding such charms,
A thrill must have passed through your withered old
     arms!
I looked and I longed and I wished in despair;
I wished myself turned to a cane-bottomed chair.

It was but a moment she sat in this place;
She'd a scarf on her neck and a smile on her face:
A smile on her face, and a rose in her hair,
And she sat there and bloomed in my cane-bottomed
     chair.

And so I have valued my chair ever since,
Like the shrine of a saint or the throne of a prince;
Saint Fanny, my patroness sweet, I declare,
The queen of my heart and my cane-bottomed chair.

When the candles burn low, and the company's gone,
In the silence of night, as I sit here alone—
I sit here alone, but we yet are a pair—
My Fanny I see in my cane-bottomed chair.

She comes from the past and revisits my room;
She looks as she then did—all beauty and bloom;
So smiling and tender, so fresh and so fair—
And yonder she sits in my cane-bottomed chair.

THE MAHOGANY TREE

CHRISTMAS is here;
  Winds whistle shrill,
Icy and chill,—
Little care we;
Little we fear
  Weather without,—
  Shelter about
    The Mahogany-tree.

Once on the boughs
  Birds of rare plumes
  Sang, in its bloom:
Night-birds are we;
Here we carouse,
  Singing like them,
  Perched round the stem
    Of the jolly old tree.

Here let us sport,
  Boys, as we sit;
  Laughter and wit
    Flashing so free.
Life is but short;
  When we are gone,
  Let them sing on
    Round the old tree.

Evenings we knew,
  Happy as this;
  Faces we miss,
    Pleasant to see.
Kind hearts and true,
  Gentle and just,
  Peace to your dust!
    We sing round the tree.

Care, like a dun,
  Lurks at the gate:
  Let the dog wait;
    Happy we'll be!
Drink, every one;
  Pile up the coals,
  Fill the red bowls,
    Round the old tree!

Drain we the cup—
  Friend, art afraid?
  Spirits are laid
    In the Red Sea.
Mantle it up;
  Empty it yet:
  Let us forget,
    Round the old tree.

Sorrows, begone!
  Life and its ills,
  Duns and their bills,
    Bid we to flee.
Come with the dawn,
  Blue-devil sprite:
  Leave us to-night,
    Round the old tree.

THEOCRITUS

THEOCRITUS, famous Greek poet, born in Syracuse about the middle of the third century before Christ. He went to Egypt, where he was a favorite of King Ptolemy Philadelphus. He later returned to his native land. His works, as they have come down to us, number thirty idyls and twenty-two epigrams.

THE SONGS OF THE REAPERS

(From "The Tenth Idyl."—Translated by Andrew Lang)

BATTUS—Ye Muses Pierian, sing ye with me the slender maiden; for whatsoever ye do but touch, ye goddesses, ye make wholly fair.

They all call thee a *gipsy,* gracious Bombyca, and *lean,* and sunburnt; 'tis only I that call thee *honey-pale.*

Yea, and the violet is swart, and swart the lettered hyacinth, but yet these flowers are chosen the first in garlands.

The goat runs after cytisus, the wolf pursues the goat, the crane follows the plough, but I am wild for love of thee.

Would it were mine, all the wealth whereof once Croesus was lord, as men tell! Then images of us twain, all in gold, should be dedicated to Aphrodite, —thou with thy flute, and a rose, yea, or an apple, and I in fair attire, and new shoon of Amyclae on both my feet.

Ah, gracious Bombyca, thy feet are fashioned like carven ivory; thy voice is drowsy sweet; and thy ways, I cannot tell of them! . . .

Demeter, rich in fruit, and rich in grain, may this corn be easy to win, and fruitful exceedingly!

Bind, ye bandsters, the sheaves, lest the wayfarer should cry, "Men of straw were the workers here, ay, and their hire was wasted!"

See that the cut stubble faces the North wind, or the West: 'tis thus the grain waxes richest.

They that thresh corn should shun the noonday sleep; at noon the chaff parts easiest from the straw.

As for the reapers, let them begin when the crested lark is waking, and cease when he sleeps, but take holiday in the heat.

Boil the lentils better, thou miserly stewart; take heed lest thou chop thy fingers, when thou'rt splitting cumin-seed.

EDITH M. THOMAS

EDITH MATILDA THOMAS, an American poetess, was born in Chatham, Ohio, in 1854. She was educated at the State Normal Institute. As a girl she was a frequent contributor to the local newspapers. In 1885 she published "A New Year's Masque," a volume that established her position in the literary world. Other volumes followed. She is a writer of critical prose as well as of verse.

SYRINX

(From "A New Year's Message, and Other Poems." Copyright, 1884, by Edith M. Thomas. Houghton, Mifflin & Co., Publishers)

COME forth, too timid spirit of the reed!
    Leave thy plashed coverts and elusions shy,
And find delight at large in grove and mead.
    No ambushed harm, no wanton, peering eye;
The shepherd's uncouth god thou need'st not fear—
Pan has not passed this way for many a year.

'Tis but the vagrant wind that makes thee start—
    The pleasure-loving south, the freshening west;
The willow-woven veil they softly part
    To fan the lily on the stream's warm breast;
No ruder stir, no footstep pressing near—
Pan has not passed this way for many a year.

Whether he lies in some mossed wood, asleep,
    And heeds not how the acorns drop around,
Or in some shelly cavern near the deep,
    Lulled by its pulses of eternal sound,

He wakes not, answers not our sylvan cheer—
Pan has been gone this many a silent year.

Else we had seen him, through the mists of morn,
  To upland pasture lead his bleating charge:
There is no shag upon the stunted thorn,
  No hoof-print on the river's silver marge;
Nor broken branch of pine, nor ivied spear—
Pan has not passed that way for many a year.

O tremulous elf, reach me a hollow pipe,
  The best and smoothest of thy mellow store.
Now I may blow till Time be hoary ripe,
  And listening streams forsake the paths they
    wore.
Pan loved the sound, but now will never hear—
Pan has not trimmed a reed this many a year.

And so, come freely forth, and through the sedge
  Lift up a dimpled, warm, Arcadian face,
As on that day when fear thy feet did fledge,
  And thou didst safely win the breathless race. . . .
I am deceived: nor Pan nor thou art here—
Pan has been gone this many a silent year.

THE GRASSHOPPER

(From " A New Year's Message, and Other Poems." Copyright,
  1884, by Edith M. Thomas. Houghton, Mifflin & Co., Publishers)

SHUTTLE of the sunburnt grass,
  Fifer in the dun cuirass,
Fifing shrilly in the morn,
Shrilly still at eve unworn;
Now to rear, now in the van,
Gayest of the elfin clan:

Though I watch their rustling flight,
I can never guess aright
Where their lodging-places are:
'Mid some daisy's golden star,
Or beneath a roofing leaf,
Or in fringes of a sheaf,
Tenated as soon as bound!
Loud thy reveille doth sound.
When the earth is laid asleep,
And her dreams are passing deep,
On mid-August afternoons;
And through all the harvest moons,
Nights brimmed up with honeyed peace,—
Thy gainsaying doth not cease.
When the frost comes thou art dead:
We along the stubble tread,
On blue, frozen morns, and note
No least murmur is afloat;
Wondrous still our fields are then,
Fifer of the elfin men.

LYOF N. TOLSTOY

Count Lyof Nikolaevitch Tolstoy, one of the greatest writers of the present day, was born near Tula, Russia, in 1828. He was educated at the University of Kazan; served in the Russian Army and fought at Sebastopol. His novels make a long list, and each volume has been hailed with applause by the readers of many countries besides his own. He is an intense realist, a teacher. He has radical views on politics and religion, that could be only adopted if human nature itself were changed, but his views are, nevertheless, most interesting reading, and have had marked effect on present social conditions in Russia.

THE BEGGARS OF MOSCOW

(From "What Must We Do Then")

HAVING passed the greater part of my life in the country, I came at length, in the year 1881, to reside in Moscow, where I was immediately struck with the extreme state of pauperism in that city. Though well acquainted with the privations of the poor in rural districts, I had not the faintest conception of their actual condition in towns.

In Moscow it is impossible to pass a street without meeting beggars of a peculiar kind quite unlike those in the country, who go about there, as the saying is, "with a bag and the name of Christ."

The Moscow beggars neither carry a bag nor ask for alms. In most cases when they meet you, they only try to catch your eye, and act according to the expression of your face.

I know of one such, a bankrupt gentleman. He is

an old man, who advances slowly, limping painfully on each leg. When he meets you, he limps, and makes a bow. If you stop, he takes off his cap, furnished with a cockade, bows again, and begs. If you do not stop, he pretends only to be lame, and continues limping along.

That is a specimen of a genuine Moscow beggar, and an experienced one.

At first I did not know why such mendicants did not ask openly; but afterwards I learned why, without understanding the reason. One day I saw a policeman push a ragged peasant, all swollen from dropsy, into a cab. I asked what he had been doing, and the policeman replied,—

" Begging."

" Is begging, then, forbidden? "

" So it seems," he answered. As the man was being driven away, I took another cab, and followed. I wished to find out whether mendicancy was really forbidden, and if so, why it was? I could not at all understand how it was possible to forbid one man asking something from another; and, moreover. I had my doubts whether it was illegal in a city where it flourished to such an extent.

I entered the police-station where the pauper had been taken, and asked an official armed with sword and pistol, and seated at a table, what he had been arrested for.

The man looked up at me sharply, and said, " What business is that of yours? "

However, feeling the necessity of some explanation, he added, " The authorities order such fellows to be arrested, so I suppose it is necessary."

I went away. The policeman who had brought the man was sitting in the window of the ante-room, studying his note-book. I said to him,—

" Is it really true that poor people are not allowed to ask for alms in Christ's name? "

The man started, as if waking up from a sleep, stared at me, then relapsed again into a state of stolid indifference, and, reseating himself on the window-sill, said,—

"The authorities require it, so you see it is necessary."

And as he became again absorbed in his note-book, I went down the steps towards my cab.

"Well! have they locked him up?" asked the cabman. He had evidently become interested in the matter.

"They have," I answered. He shook his head.

"Is begging, then, forbidden here in Moscow?" I asked.

"I can't tell you," he said.

"How," I said, "can a man be locked up, for begging in the name of Christ?"

"Nowadays things have changed, and you see it is forbidden," he answered.

Since that time, I have seen policemen several times taking paupers to the police-station, and thence to the work-house: indeed, I once met a whole crowd of these poor creatures, about thirty, escorted before and behind by policemen. I asked what they had been doing.

"Begging," was the reply.

It appears that, according to law, mendicancy is forbidden in Moscow, notwithstanding the great number of beggars one meets there in every street, whole rows of them near the churches during service-time, and most of all at funerals. But why are some caught and locked up, while others are let alone? This I have not been able to solve. Either there are lawful and unlawful beggars amongst them, or else there are so many that it is impossible to catch them all; or, perhaps, though some are taken up, others fill their places.

There are a great variety of such mendicants in

Moscow. There are those that make a living by begging. There are also honestly destitute people, such as have somehow chanced to reach Moscow, and are really in extreme need.

Amongst these last are men and women evidently from the country. I have often met such. Some of them who had fallen ill, and afterward recovered and left the hospital, could now find no means, either of feeding themselves, or of getting away from Moscow; some of them, besides, had taken to drink (such probably was the case of the man with dropsy whom I met); some were in good health, but had been burned out of house and home, or else were very old, or were widowed or deserted women with children; some others were sound as to health, and quite capable of working.

These robust fellows especially interested me,—the more so, because, since my arrival in Moscow, I had, for the sake of exercise, contracted the habit of going to the Sparrow Hills, and working there with two peasants who sawed wood. These men were exactly like the beggars whom I often met in the streets. One was called Peter, and was an ex-soldier from Kaluga; the other, Simon, from Vladimir. They possessed nothing save the clothes on their backs: and they earned, by working very hard, from forty to forty-five kopeks a day; out of this they both put a little aside,—the Kaluga soldier, in order to buy a fur coat; the Vladímir peasant, in order to get money enough to return to his home in the country.

Meeting, therefore, in the streets similar individuals, I was particularly interested in them, and failed to understand why some begged whilst others worked.

Whenever I met a beggar of this description, I used to ask him how it was that he had come to such a state. Once I met a strong, healthy-looking peasant: he asked alms. I questioned him as to who he was, and whence he had come.

He told me he had come from Kaluga, in search of work. He had at first found some, such as sawing old timber into fire-wood; but after he and his companion had finished the job, though they had continually looked for more work, they had not found any; his companion had left him, and he himself had passed a fortnight in the utmost need, and, having sold all he possessed to obtain food, had not now enough, even to buy the tools necessary for sawing.

I gave him the money for a saw, and told him where to go for work. I had previously arranged with Peter and Simon that they should accept a new fellow-worker, and find him a companion.

"Be sure you come! There is plenty of work to be done," I said on parting.

"You may depend on me," he answered. "Do you think there can be any pleasure in knocking about, begging, if I could work?"

The man solemnly promised that he would come; and he seemed to be honest, and really meaning to work.

Next day, on coming to my friends, Peter and Simon, I asked them whether the man had arrived. They said he had not; nor, indeed, did he come at all: and in this way I was frequently deceived.

I have also been deceived by those who stated that they only wanted a little money to buy a ticket, in order to return home, and whom I again met in the streets a few days later. Many of them I came to know well, and they knew me; though occasionally, having forgotten me, they would repeat the same false tale; but sometimes they would turn away on recognizing me.

In this way I discovered, that, even in this class of men, there are many rogues.

But still, these poor rogues were also very much to be pitied: they were all of them ragged, hungry paupers; they are of the sort who die of cold in the streets, or hang themselves to escape living, as the papers frequently tell us.

When I talked to my town friends about this pauperism which surrounded them, they always replied, "Oh! you have seen nothing yet! You should go to the Khitrof Market, and visit the lodging-houses there, if you want to see the genuine 'Golden Company.'"

One jovial friend of mine added, that the number of these paupers had so increased, that they already formed, not a "Golden Company," but a "Golden Regiment."

My lively friend was right; but he would have been yet nearer the truth had he said that these men formed, in Moscow, not a company, nor a regiment, but a whole army,—an army, I should judge, of about fifty thousand.

The regular townspeople, when they spoke to me about the pauperism of the city, always seemed to feel a certain pleasure or pride in being able to give me such precise information.

I remember I noticed, when visiting London, that the citizens there seemed also to find a certain satisfaction in telling me about London destitution, as though it were something to be proud of.

However, wishing to inspect this poverty about which I had heard so much, I turned my steps very often towards the Khitrof Market; but, on each occasion, I felt a sensation of pain and shame. "Why should you go to look at the suffering of human beings whom you cannot help?" said one voice within me. "If you live here, and see all that is pleasant in town life, go and see also what is wretched," replied another.

And so, one cold, windy day in December, two years ago, I went to the Khitrof Market, the center of the town pauperism.

It was on a week-day, about four in the afternoon. While still a good distance off, I noticed greater and greater numbers of men in strange garb, evidently not originally meant for them; and in yet stranger foot-apparel, men of a peculiar unhealthy complexion, and all apparently showing a remarkable indifference to all that surrounded them.

Men in the strangest, most incongruous costumes sauntered along, evidently without the least thought as to how they might look in the eyes of others. They were all going in the same direction. Without asking the way, which was unknown to me, I followed them, and came to the Khitrof Market.

There I found women likewise in ragged capes, rough-looking cloaks, jackets, boots, and goloshes. Perfectly free and easy in their manner, notwithstanding the grotesque monstrosity of their attire, these women, old and young, were sitting, bargaining, strolling about, and abusing one another.

Market-time having evidently passed, there were not many people there; and as most of them were going up-hill, through the market-place, and all in the same direction, I followed them.

The farther I went, the greater became the stream of people flowing into the one road. Having passed the market, and gone up the street, I found that I was following two women, one old, the other young. Both were clothed in some gray ragged stuff. They were talking, as they walked, about some kind of business.

Every expression was unfailingly accompanied by some obscene word. They were neither of them drunk, but were absorbed with their own affairs; and the men passing, and those about them, paid not the slightest attention to their language, which sounded so strange to me. It appeared to be the generally accepted manner of speech in those parts. On the left we passed some private night-lodging-houses, and some of the crowd entered them: others continued to ascend the hill towards a large corner house. The majority of the people walking along with me went into this house. In front of it, people all of the same sort were standing and sitting, on the sidewalk and in the snow.

At the right of the entrance were women; at the left, men. I passed by the men: I passed by the women (there were several hundreds in all), and stopped where the crowd ceased.

This building was the "Liapin free night-lodging-house." The crowd was composed of night-lodgers, waiting to be let in. At five o'clock in the evening this house is opened and the crowd admitted. Hither came almost all the people whom I followed.

I remained standing where the file of men ended. Those nearest to me stared at me till I had to look at them. The remnants of garments covering their bodies were very various; but the one expression of the eyes of all alike seemed to be, "Why have you, a man from another world, stopped here with us? Who are you? Are you a self-satisfied man of wealth, desiring to be gladdened by the sight of our need, to divert yourself in your idleness, and to mock at us? or are you that which does not and can not exist,—a man who pities us?"

On all their faces the same question was written. Each would look at me, meet my eyes, and turn away again.

I wanted to speak to some one of them, but for a long time I could not summon up courage. However, eventually our mutual exchange of glances introduced us to each other; and we felt that, however widely separated were our social positions in life, after all we were fellow-men, and so ceased to be afraid of one another.

Next to me stood a peasant with a swollen face, and red beard, in a ragged jacket, and worn-out goloshes on his naked feet, though there were eight degrees of frost. For the third or fourth time our eyes met; and I felt so drawn to him that I was no longer ashamed to address him (to have refrained from doing so would have been the only real shame), and asked him where he came from.

He answered eagerly, while a crowd began to collect round us, that he had come from Smolensk in search of work, in order to be able to buy bread, and pay his taxes.

"There is no work to be had nowadays," he said: "the soldiers have got hold of it all. So here am I knocking about; and God is my witness, I have not had any thing to eat for two days."

He said this shyly, with an attempt at a smile. A seller of warm drinks, an old soldier, was standing near. I called him, and made him pour out a glass for him. The peasant took the warm vessel in his hands, and, before drinking, warmed them against the glass, trying not to lose any of the precious heat; and whilst doing this he related to me his story.

The adventures of these people, or at least the stories which they tell, are almost always the same: He had had a little work; then it had ceased: and here, in the night-lodging-house, his purse, containing his money and passport, had been stolen from him. Now he could not leave Moscow.

He told me that during the day he warmed himself in public-houses, eating any stale crust of bread which might be given him. His night's lodging here in Liapin's house cost him nothing.

He was only waiting for the round of the police-sergeant to lock him up for being without his passport, when he would be sent on foot, with a party of men similarly situated, to the place of his birth.

" They say the inspection will take place on Thursday, when I shall be taken up; so I must try and keep on until then." ('The prison and his compulsory journey appeared to him as the "promised land.") While he was speaking, two or three men in the crowd said they were also in exactly the same situation.

A thin, pale youth, with a long nose, only a shirt upon his back, and that torn about the shoulders, and a tattered cap on his head, edged his way to me through the crowd. He was shivering violently all the time, but tried, as he caught my eye, to smile scornfully at the peasant's talk, thinking thus to show his superiority.

I offered him some drink.

He warmed his hands on the tumbler as the other had done; but just as he began to speak, he was shouldered aside by a big, black, hook-nosed, bareheaded fellow, in a thin shirt and waistcoat, who also asked for some drink.

Then a tall old man, with a thin beard, in an overcoat fastened round the waist with a cord, and in matting-shoes, had some. He was drunk.

Then came a little man, with a swollen face and teary eyes, in a coarse brown jacket, and with knees protruding through his torn trousers, and knocking against each other with cold. He shivered so that he could not hold the glass, and spilled the contents over his clothes: the others took to abusing him, but he only grinned miserably, and shivered.

After him came an ugly, deformed man in rags, and with bare feet. Then an individual of the officer type; another belonging to the church class; then a strange-looking being without a nose,—and all of them hungry, cold, suppliant, and humble,—crowded round me, and stretched out their hands for the glass; but the drink was exhausted. Then one man asked for money: I gave him some. A second and a third followed, till the whole crowd pressed on me. In the general confusion the gatekeeper of the neighboring house shouted to the crowd to clear the pavement before his house, and the people submissively obeyed.

Some of them undertook to control the tumult, and took me under their protection. They attempted to drag me out of the crush. But the crowd that formerly had lined the pavement in a long file, now had become condensed about me. Every one looked at me and begged; and it seemed as if each face were more pitiful, harassed, and degraded than the other. I distributed all the money I had,—only about twenty rubles,—and entered the lodging-house with the crowd. The house was enormous, and consisted of four parts. In the upper stories were the men's rooms; on the ground-floor the women's. I went first into the women's dormitory,—a large room filled with beds resembling the berths in a third-class railway-carriage. They were arranged in two tiers, one above the other.

Strange-looking women in ragged dresses, without jackets, old and young, kept coming in and occupying places, some below, others climbing above. Some of the elder ones crossed themselves, pronouncing the name of the founder of the refuge. Some laughed and swore.

I went up-stairs. There, in a similar way, the men had taken their places. Amongst them I recognized one of those to whom I had given money. On seeing him I suddenly felt horribly ashamed, and made haste to leave.

ANTHONY TROLLOPE

ANTHONY TROLLOPE, English novelist, was born in
Harrow in 1815; died in London in 1862. He traveled much in his youth, and the impressions of his
wanderings appeared in several books on various
countries of which he had made a study. His first
novel, entitled "The Kellys and the O'Kellys," was
published in 1847. "The Warden," published in
1855, gave him an assured place in English literature. He dealt with various classes of English
society and his delineation of character was mas-
terly. Among his best books are the "Barchester"
series, "The Prime Minister" and "The Claver-
ings."

THE DUKE OF OMNIUM

(From "The Prime Minister")

THE night of the debate arrived, but before the
debate was commenced Sir Timothy Beeswax
got up to make a personal explanation. He thought
it right to state to the House how it came to pass
that he found himself bound to leave the ministry
at so important a crisis in its existence. Then an
observation was made by an honorable member of
the government—presumably in a whisper, but still
loud enough to catch the sharp ears of Sir Timothy,
who now sat just below the gangway. It was said
afterward that the gentleman who made the observation—an Irish gentleman named Fitzgibbon, conspicuous rather for his loyalty to his party than his
steadiness—had purposely taken the place in which

ne then sat, that Sir Timothy might hear the whisper.
The whisper suggested that falling houses were often
left by certain animals. It was certainly a very
loud whisper, but if gentlemen are to be allowed
to whisper at all, it is almost impossible to restrain
the volume of the voice. To restrain Mr. Fitzgibbon
had always been found difficult. Sir Timothy, who
did not lack pluck, turned at once upon his assailant
and declared that words had been used with refer-
ence to himself which the honorable member did not
dare to get upon his legs and repeat. Larry Fitzgibbon, as the gentleman was called, looked him full
in the face, but did not move his hat from his head
or stir a limb. It was a pleasant little episode in
the evening's work, and afforded satisfaction to the
House generally. Then Sir Timothy went on with
his explanation. The details of this measure, as
soon as they were made known to him, appeared to
him, he said, to be fraught with the gravest and
most pernicious consequences. He was sure that the
members of her majesty's government, who were
hurrying on this measure with what he thought was
indecent haste—ministers are always either indecent
in their haste or treacherous in their delay—had
not considered what they were doing, or, if they had
considered, were blind as to its results. He then attempted to discuss the details of the measure, but
was called to order. A personal explanation could
not be allowed to give him an opportunity of an-
ticipating the debate. He contrived, however, before
he sat down to say some very heavy things against
his late chief, and especially to congratulate the
duke on the services of the honorable gentleman, the
member for Mayo, meaning thereby Mr. Laurence
Fitzgibbon.

It would, perhaps have been well for everybody if
the measure could have been withdrawn and the
ministry could have resigned without the debate, as

everybody was convinced what would be the end of it. Let the second reading go as it might, the bill could not be carried. There are measures which require the hopeful heartiness of a new ministry, and thorough-going energy of a young Parliament, and this was one of them. The House was as fully agreed that this change was necessary as it ever is agreed on any subject, but still the thing could not be done. Even Mr. Monk, who was the most earnest of men, felt the general slackness of all around him. The commotion and excitement which would be caused by a change of ministry might restore its proper tone to the House, but at its present condition it was unfit for the work. Nevertheless, Mr. Monk made his speech, and put all his arguments into lucid order. He knew it was for nothing, but nevertheless it must be done. For hour after hour he went on, for it was necessary to give every detail of his contemplated proposition. He went through it as sedulously as though he had expected to succeed, and sat down about nine o'clock in the evening. Then Sir Orlando moved the adjournment of the House till the morrow, giving as his reason for doing so the expedience of considering the details he had heard. To this no opposition was made, and the House was adjourned.

On the following day the clubs were all alive with rumors as to the coming debate. It was known that a strong party had been formed under the auspices of Sir Orlando, and that with him Sir Timothy and other politicians were in close council. It was, of course, necessary that they should impart to many the secrets of their conclave, so that it was known early in the afternoon that it was the intention of the Opposition not to discuss the bill, but to move that it be read a second time that day six months. The ministry had hardly expected this, as the bill was undoubtedly popular both in the

House and in the country; and if the Opposition should be beaten in such a course, that defeat would tend greatly to strengthen the hands of the government. But, if the foe could succeed in carrying a positive veto on the second reading, it would, under all the circumstances, be tantamount to a vote of want of confidence. "I'm afraid they know almost more than we do as to the feeling of members," said Mr. Roby to Mr. Rattler.

"There isn't a man in the House whose feeling in the matter I don't know," said Rattler, "but I'm not quite so sure of their principles. On our own side, in our own party, there are a score of men who detest the duke though they would fain be true to the government. They have voted with him through thick and thin, and he has not spoken a word to one of them since he became prime minister. What are you to do with such a man? How are you to act with him?"

"Lupton wrote to him the other day about something," answered the other, "I forget what, and he got a note back from Warburton as cold as ice—an absolute slap in the face. Fancy treating a man like Lupton in that way—one of the most popular men in the House, related to half the peerage, and a man who thinks so much of himself! I shouldn't wonder if he were to vote against us; I shouldn't, indeed."

"It has all been the old duke's doing," said Rattler, "and, no doubt, it was intended for the best; but the thing has been a failure from the beginning to the end. I knew it would be so. I don't think there has been a single man who has understood what a ministerial coalition really means, except you and I. From the very beginning, all your men were averse to it in spirit."

"Look how they were treated!" said Mr. Roby. "Was it likely that they should be very stanch when Mr. Monk became leader of the House?"

There was a cabinet council that day which lasted but a few minutes, and it may be easily presumed that the ministers decided that they would all resign at once if Sir Orlando should carry his amendment. It is not unlikely that they were agreed to do the same if he should nearly carry it, leaving probably the prime minister to judge what narrow majority would constitute nearness. On this occasion all the gentlemen assembled were jocund in their manner, and apparently well satisfied, as though they saw before them an end to all their troubles. The Spartan boy did not even make a grimace when the wolf bit him beneath his frock, and these were all Spartan boys. Even the prime minister, who had fortified himself for the occasion, and who never wept in any company but that of his wife and his old friend, was pleasant in his manner, and almost affable. "We sha'n't make this step toward the millennium just at present," he said to Phineas Finn, as they left the room together—referring to words which Phineas had spoken on a former occasion, and which then had not been very well taken.

"But we shall have made a step toward the step," said Phineas, "and in getting to a millennium, even that is something."

"I suppose we are all too anxious," said the duke, "to see some great effects come from our own little doings. Good-day. We shall know all about it tolerably early. Monk seems to think that it will be an attack on the ministry, and not on the bill, and that it will be best to get a vote with as little delay as possible."

"I'll bet an even five-pound note," said Mr. Lupton, at the Carlton, "that the present ministry is out to-morrow, and another, that no one names five members of the next Cabinet."

"You can help to win your first bet," said Mr. Beauchamp, a very old member, who, like many

other Conservatives, had supported the coalition.
"I shall not do that," said Lupton, "though I
think I ought. I won't vote against the man in his
misfortunes, though, upon my soul, I don't love
him very dearly. I shall vote neither way, but I
hope that Sir Orlando may succeed."

"If he does, who is to come in?" said the other.
"I suppose you don't want to serve under Sir
Orlando?"

"Nor certainly under the Duke of Omnium. We
shall not want a prime minister as long as there are
as good fish in the sea as have been caught out of
it."

There had lately been formed a new Liberal club,
established on a broader basis than the Progress,
and perhaps with a greater amount of aristocratic
support. This had come up since the duke had been
prime minister. Certain busy men have never been
quite contented with the existing state of things,
and had thought that the Liberal party, with such
assistance as such club could give it, would be strong
enough to rule alone. That the great Liberal party
should be impeded in its work and its triumph by
such men as Sir Orlando Drought and Sir Timothy
Beeswax was odious to the club. All the Pallisers
had, from time immemorial, run straight as Liberals,
and, therefore, the club had been unwilling to op-
pose the duke personally, though he was the chief of
the coalition. And certain members of the Gover-
ment—Phineas Finn, for instance, Barrington Erle,
and Mr. Rattler—were on the committee of the club.
But the club, as a club, was not averse to a discon-
tinuance of the present state of things. Mr. Gres-
ham might again become prime minister, if he would
condescend so far, or Mr. Monk. It might be possible that the great Liberal triumph contemplated by
the club might not be achieved by the present
House; but the present House must go shortly, and

then, with that assistance from a well-organized club, which had lately been so terribly wanting—the lack of which had made the coalition necessary—no doubt the British constituencies would do their duty, and a Liberal prime minister, pure and simple, might reign—almost forever. With this great future before it, the club was very lukewarm in its support of the present bill. "I shall go down and vote for them, of course," said Mr. O'Mahony, "just for the look of the thing." In saying this, Mr. O'Mahony expressed the feeling of the club, and the feeling of the Liberal party generally. There was something due to the duke, but not enough to make it incumbent on his friends to maintain him in his position as prime minister. . . .

Early in the night—before twelve o'clock—the House divided, and even at the moment of the division no one quite knew how it would go. There would be many who would, of course, vote against the amendment, as being simply desirous of recording their opinion in favor of the bill generally. And there were some who thought that Sir Orlando and his followers had been too forward and too confident of their own standing in the House, in trying so violent a mode of opposition. It would have been better, these men thought, to have insured success by a gradual and persistent opposition to the bill itself. But they hardly knew how thoroughly men may be alienated by silence and a cold demeanor. Sir Orlando on the division was beaten, but was beaten only by nine. "He can't go on with his bill," said Rattler, in one of the lobbies of the House. "I defy him. The House wouldn't stand it, you know." "No minister," said Roby, "could carry a measure like that with a majority of nine on a vote of confidence!" The House was, of course, adjourned, and Mr. Monk went at once to Carlton Terrace.

"I wish it had only been three or four," said the duke, laughing.

"Why so?"

"Because there would have been less doubt."

"Is there any at present?"

"Less possibility for doubt, I will say. You would not wish to make the attempt with such a majority?"

"I could not do it, duke!"

"I quite agree with you. But there will be those who will say that the attempt might be made; who will accuse us of being faint-hearted because we do not make it."

"They will be men who understand nothing of the temper of the House."

"Very likely. But still, I wish the majority had only been two or three. There is little more to be said, I suppose."

"Very little, your grace."

"We had better meet to-morrow at two, and, if possible, I will see her majesty in the afternoon. Good-night, Mr. Monk."

"Good-night, duke."

"My reign is ended. You are a good deal older man than I, and yet, probably, yours has yet to begin." Mr. Monk smiled, and shook his head as he left the room, not trusting himself to discuss so large a subject at so late an hour of the night.

Without waiting a moment after his colleague's departure, the prime minister—for he was still prime minister—went into his wife's room, knowing that she was waiting up till she should hear the result of the division, and there he found Mrs. Finn with her. "Is it over?" asked the duchess.

"Yes; there has been a division. Mr. Monk has just been with me."

"Well!"

"We have beaten them, of course, as we always

do," said the duke, attempting to be pleasant. "You didn't suppose there was anything to fear? Your husband has always bid you keep up your courage, has he not, Mrs. Finn?"

"My husband has lost his senses, I think," she said. "He has taken to such storming and raving about his political enemies that I hardly dare to open my mouth."

"Tell me what has been done, Plantagenet," ejaculated the duchess.

"Don't you be as unreasonable as Mrs. Finn, Cora. The House has voted against Sir Orlando's amendment by a majority of nine."

"Only nine!"

"And I shall cease to be prime minister to-morrow."

IVAN TURGENIEFF

IVAN SERGEYEVICH TURGENIEFF, Russian novelist,
born in Orel in 1818; died near Paris in 1883. He
was in the government service, but on account of his
political opinions was banished. He lived the latter
part of his life in Paris. Among his books may be
mentioned "Fathers and Sons," "Smoke," "A Lear
of the Steppe" and "Dimitri Rodin." He was the
first writer to use the term "Nihilist" in its present
political sense.

GREGORY'S RETURN TO TITIANA

(From "First Love")

I ONCE entered the hut of a peasant-woman who
had just lost her only son; to my great surprise, I found her calm, almost cheerful. "Do not
wonder," said her husband, who doubtless noticed
the impression made upon me; "she now is ossified."
Litvinof was thus "ossified"—a perfect calm had
taken possession of him during the first few hours
of his journey. Entirely worn out, almost unconscious, he was yet alive, after all the pain and tor-
ture of the last week, after all the blows that had
fallen, one after another, upon him. He was not
one who could, with impunity, receive such blows.

He had now no plan before him; he tried to drive
all thought from his mind; he was going to Russia
because he must go somewhere; but he had no object in going thither. He had lost all sense of his
own individuality; he took no notice of his own acts.
It seemed to him sometimes as though he were carry-

ing about with him his dead body; it was only a painful sense of hopeless grief that convinced him he was still alive. Sometimes it seemed impossible to him that a woman, that passion, could have so influenced him. . . .

"What shameful weakness!" he murmured, and throwing back his cloak, he settled himself more comfortably in his seat. He must now begin a new life, he thought. A moment more, and he was smiling bitterly, astonished at himself. He looked out of the window. It was an unpleasant day; it did not rain, but the fog was dense and low clouds covered the sky. The train was moving against the wind; clouds of smoke, now light, now dark, rolled by the window. Litvinof watched these clouds. Ceaselessly they rose and fell, clinging to the grass and bushes, stretching themselves out, melting in the damp air, or whirling about in eddies, ever changing, yet ever the same. Sometimes the wind changed, or the road made a turn, then all this mass of vapor would suddenly disappear, only to be seen again immediately, on the other side, and, in an interminable cloud, hide from view the valley of the Rhine.

Litvinof continued to gaze in silence; an odd fancy had taken possession of him. He was alone in the carriage, there was no one to listen to him. "Smoke! smoke!" he kept repeating to himself, and suddenly all the past seemed like smoke to him: his whole life, his life in Russia; all that was human, but chiefly all that was Russian in his experience. "All was but smoke and vapor," he thought: "everything is constantly changing, one shape resolves itself into another, one event succeeds another, but in reality everything remains the same. There is much stir and confusion, but all these clouds vanish at last without leaving any trace, without having accomplished anything. The wind changes its direction, they pass to the other side and then continue

246

their feverish and fruitless motion." He remembered what had taken place during the last few years, and how great had been the tumult and excitement. . . . "Smoke," he muttered; "smoke." He remembered the noisy and disorderly discussions in Goubaref's room, and the disputes which he had heard between other persons, of high and low degree, radical and conservative, old and young. . . .

"Smoke!" he repeated; "smoke and vapor!" He thought finally of the famous picnic, of the speeches and arguments of the statesmen there, and also of Potoughine's long disquisitions.

"Smoke! smoke!" he cried, "and nothing more." Then his own efforts, his desires, his trials, and his dreams all came before his mind. The memory of these served only to provoke a gesture of discouragement.

Meanwhile the train was rushing on. Rastadt, Carlsruhe, and Bruchsal were already far behind him; on the right the mountains retreated in the distance, then approached again, but they were now less lofty and not covered with trees as before. The train made a short turn; they were at Heidelberg. The carriage glided into the station; the news-dealers began to cry all kinds of papers, even those of Russian origin. Many of the travelers stepped out upon the platform and walked about, but Litvinof did not leave his place; he was sitting there with his head bowed down. . . .

During the night he passed through Cassel. As the twilight deepened into darkness, an intolerable agony preyed like a vulture at his heart. He began to weep, with his head buried in one corner of the carriage. His tears flowed for a long time, without, however, affording him any relief.

During this time, in a hotel at Cassel, Tatiana was lying on a bed, burning with fever; Capitoline Markovna was standing near her.

"Tania," she said to her, "do let me send a telegram to Gregory Mikhailovitch; do let me, Tania."

"No, aunt," she answered, "you must not. Do not be frightened. Give me some water; I shall soon be better."

In fact, a week afterward, she had quite recovered, and the aunt and niece proceeded on their journey.

*　　*　　*　　*　　*　　*　　*

Without stopping either at St. Petersburg or Moscow, Litvinof returned to his humble home. He was startled when he first saw his father, he appeared so old and broken down. The old man, on seeing his son again, was as much delighted as one so near the close of life could be. He hastened to give him charge of his affairs, which were in great disorder, and, after a few weeks of sickness and pain, passed quietly away. Litvinof now was left alone in the old family home; he began to improve his lands, with an aching heart, without any liking for his work, without hope, without money. The management of an estate in Russia is no pleasant task, as too many of us know. We will not therefore enter too minutely into the difficulties which Litvinof encountered. It was impossible for him to introduce improvements and reforms; the application of that knowledge which he had acquired in foreign countries had to be indefinitely postponed; necessity compelled him to live as he could from day to day, and to make all manner of concessions, both material and moral. The new order of things worked badly, the old forms had lost their strength; inexperience had to struggle with dishonesty and fraud. The old institutions had no sustaining power, they were breaking asunder like our vast, mossy marshes: only that noble word, "Liberty!" pronounced by

the Czar, floated over them, as the spirit of God
once moved upon the face of the waters. It was
necessary, above all else, to have patience, not pas-
sive, but diligent, persistent, and indomitable patience. This was doubly painful to Litvinof, in the
state of mind in which he found himself. Life had
few attractions for him . . . could labor, then,
present him any?

A year passed by, a second followed it, the third
had already begun its course. The grand thought
of emancipation was commencing to produce its
fruits, to influence the customs of the people. The
seed that had been sown had sprouted and appeared above the ground and could now no more
be trampled on by either an open or a secret enemy.
Although Litvinof finally rented to the peasants
the greater portion of his land on shares, and although this land was all cultivated in the primitive
manner, yet he met with some success. He started
his manufactory, worked a small farm with five
free laborers whom he had finally selected after trying forty, and paid off his heaviest debts. His
natural powers returned to him; he began to look
like himself again.

During all this time a feeling of deep sadness remained with him: he was leading a life which ill
accorded with his years; he had shut himself up
within a narrow circle, but he no longer exhibited
his former indifference to everything about him;
he walked among men like a living man. The last
traces of the charm under whose influence he had
fallen had also disappeared; and all that had taken
place at Baden now seemed to him like a dream.
And Irene . . . her image, too, had paled away
and vanished; only something vaguely dangerous
was dimly outlined through the mist which concealed
it. He rarely had news of Titiana; he only knew
that she was with her aunt at her home; which was

some distance from her own family estates; that she lived there quietly, going out but little and receiving few visitors; also that she was enjoying excellent health.

One fine May morning he was seated in his study, carelessly glancing over the last number of a paper from St. Petersburg, when his servant announced the arrival of his uncle. This uncle, a cousin of Capitoline Markovna, had just been making her a visit. He had bought an estate in Litvinof's neighborhood and was about taking possession of it. He remained several days with his nephew, and talked much with him concerning Tatiana.

On the day after his departure, Litvinof wrote to his cousin, for the first time since their separation. He asked permission to open a correspondence with her, and also stated that he hoped some time to meet her again. He waited her answer with great anxiety. . . . It came at last. Tatiana replied in a friendly manner. "If you are thinking of making us a visit," she said in closing, "we shall be very happy to see you at any time." Capitoline Markovna also sent him her regards. Litvinof evinced an almost childish joy; it was a long, long time since his heart had before beaten so gayly. Everything seemed bright and cheerful to him. When the sun rises and drives away the darkness of the night, a light breeze passes over the earth's bosom, reviving all nature with its cooling breath. Litvinof felt thus strengthened and rejoiced, by some mysterious influence. He was all smiles that day, even when overseeing his laborers and giving them their orders. He immediately began to prepare for the journey, and two weeks later was on his way to visit Tatiana. . . .

While the postilion was thus talking, Litvinof could not take his eyes from the little house. A lady dressed in white appeared on the piazza, looked out as though watching for someone, then disappeared again.

"Was it not Tatiana?"

His heart was beating violently.

"Faster! faster!" he cried to the postilion.

The postilion whipped up his horses. A few minutes more . . . and the carriage passed through an open gate. On the piazza he saw Capitoline Markovna running to meet him. Out of breath, her face red with excitement, she cried out, "I knew you, I knew you first! It was you! it was you! I knew you!"

Litvinof leaped to the ground lightly, without giving the little Cossack time to open the door for him, and hurriedly kissing Capitoline Markovna, rushed into the house, ran through the hall and dining-room . . . and found himself face to face with Tatiana. She was looking on him with a kind and gentle glance (she had grown a little thinner, which did not at all detract from her appearance), and holding out to him her hand. He did not take it, but fell on his knees before her. She had not expected this and knew not what to say or do. Tears came to her eyes; she was frightened, but at the same time there was an expression of joy upon her face.

"What is this, Gregory Mikhailovitch?" she said at last.

He was kissing the hem of her dress, recalling with a happy, contrite heart, how before at Baden he had thus fallen at her feet. But then and now!

"Tania," he cried, "Tania, can you forgive me?"

"Aunt, aunt, what does this mean?" she cried, turning toward Capitoline Markovna, who had just entered the room.

"Leave him alone, Tatiana," answered the good old lady; "do you not see he has repented?"

PUBLIUS VIRGIL

Publius Vergilius (Virgil) Maro, greatest of
Latin poets, was born near Mantua in 70 B.C.; died
at Brundusium in 19 B.C. He studied at Cremona,
Milan and Rome. In 37 B.C. he wrote the
"Eclogues," a series of pastorals that at once
brought him fame. He spent seven years on the
"Georgics," eleven on the "Æneid," one of the
world's great poems. It deals with the wanderings
of the Trojan, Æneas.

ÆNEAS DOTH MANY GREAT DEEDS
IN BATTLE

(From "Æneid," Book X)

NO dull delay holds Turnus back; but fiercely
    doth he fall
With all his host, on them of Troy, and meets them
    on the strand.
The war-horns sing. Æneas first breaks through
    the field-folks' band,
Fair omen of the fight—and lays the Latin folk
    alow.
Thero he slays, most huge of men, whose own heart
    bade him go
Against Æneas: through the links of brass the sword
    doth fare,
And through the kirtle's scaly gold, and wastes the
    side laid bare.

Then Lichas smites he, ripped erewhile from out his
    mother dead,

And hallowed, Phœbus, unto thee, because his baby
    head

Had 'scaped the steel: nor far from thence he cast-
    eth down to die

Hard Cissens, Gyas huge, who there beat down his
    company

With might of clubs; naught then availed that Her-
    culean gear,

Nor their stark hands, nor yet their sire Melampus,
    though he were

Alcides' friend so long as he on earth wrought
    heavy toil.

Lo, Pharo! while a deedless word he flingeth 'mid
    the broil,

The whirring of the javelin stays within his shout-
    ing mouth.

Thou, Cydon, following lucklessly thy new delight,
    the youth

Clytius, whose first of fallow down about his cheeks
    is spread,

Art well-nigh felled by Dardan hand, and there
    hadst thou lain dead,

At peace from all the many loves wherein thy life
    would stray,

Had not thy brethren's serried band now thrust
    across the way,

E'en Phorcus' seed: sevenfold of tale and sevenfold
    spears they wield;

But some thereof fly harmless back from helmside
    and from shield;

The rest kind Venus turned aside, that grazing past
    they flew;

But therewithal Æneas spake unto Achates true.

GEORGE WASHINGTON

GEORGE WASHINGTON, first President of the United States, born in Westmoreland County, Va., in 1732; died in Mount Vernon in 1799. His life and deeds are too well known to be related here, except so far as concerns the world of letters. His "Farewell Address" was the only thing he ever wrote that was intended for publication, but his numerous letters, and the public communications to the Continental Congress, are of great interest and value to the historical student. His diaries give an inside view of many stirring Revolutionary events.

ACCEPTING THE COMMAND OF THE ARMY

(From "A Letter to His Wife, 1775")

YOU may believe me, when I assure you in the most solemn manner that, so far from seeking this employment, I have used every effort in my power to avoid it, not only from my unwillingness to part with you and the family, but from a consciousness of its being a trust too great for my capacity; and I should enjoy more real happiness in one month with you at home than I have the most distant prospect of finding abroad, if my stay were to be seven times seven years. But as it has been a kind of destiny that has thrown me upon this service, I shall hope that my undertaking it is designed to answer some good purpose. . . .

I shall rely confidently on that Providence which has heretofore preserved and been bountiful to me, not doubting but that I shall return safe to you in the fall. I shall feel no pain from the toil or danger of the campaign; my unhappiness will flow from the uneasiness I know you will feel from being left alone. I therefore beg that you will summon your whole fortitude, and pass your time as agreeably as possible. Nothing will give me so much sincere satisfaction as to hear this, and to hear it from your own pen.

ON PROFANITY IN THE ARMY
(From " A General Order, 1775 ")

THAT the troops may have an opportunity of attending public worship, as well as to take some rest after the great fatigue they have gone through, the General in future excuses them from fatigue-duty on Sundays, except at the ship-yards, or on special occasions, until further orders. The General is sorry to be informed that the foolish and wicked practise of profane swearing—a vice heretofore little known in an American army—is growing into fashion. He hopes the officers will, by example as well as influence, endeavor to check it; and that both they and the men will reflect that we can have little hope of the blessing of Heaven upon our arms if we insult it by our impiety and folly. Added to this, it is a vice so mean and low, without any temptation, that every man of sense and character detests it.

MARK TWAIN

MARK TWAIN (SAMUEL LANGHORNE CLEMENS), best known by his pseudonym, was born in Florida, Mo., November 30, 1835. He received a common-school education, and became in turn compositor, Mississippi pilot, Confederate soldier, Nevada news-paper reporter, and finally a lecturer. Some of his best-known works are the " Innocents Abroad," 1869; " Tom Sawyer," 1876; " Huckleberry Finn," 1885; " Pudd'nhead Wilson," 1895. He is probably the most popular American humorist.

THE NOTORIOUS JUMPING FROG OF CALAVERAS COUNTY

IN compliance with the request of a friend of mine, who wrote me from the East, I called on good-natured, garrulous old Simon Wheeler, and inquired after my friend's friend, Leonidas W. Smiley, as requested to do, and I hereunto append the result. I have a lurking suspicion that *Leonidas W.* Smiley is a myth; that my friend never knew such a personage; and that he only conjec-tured that if I asked old Wheeler about him, it would remind him of his infamous *Jim* Smiley, and he would go to work and bore me to death with some exasperating reminiscence of him as long as and as tedious as it should be useless to me. If that was the design, it succeeded.

I found Simon Wheeler dozing comfortably by the barroom stove of the dilapidated tavern in the decayed mining camp of Angel's, and I noticed that he was fat and bald-headed, and had an ex-pression of winning gentleness and simplicity upon his tranquil countenance. He roused up and gave me good-day. I told him a friend of mine had commissioned me to make some inquiries about a cherished companion of his boyhood named *Leonidas W.* Smiley—*Reverend Leonidas W.* Smiley, a young minister of the Gospel, who he had heard was at one time a resident of Angel's Camp. I added that if Mr. Wheeler could tell me anything about this Reverend Leonidas W. Smiley I would feel under many obligations to him.

Simon Wheeler backed me into a corner and blockaded me there with his chair, and then sat down and reeled off the monotonous narrative which follows this paragraph. He never smiled, he never frowned, he never changed his voice from the gentle-flowing key to which he tuned his initial sentence, he never betrayed the slightest suspicion of enthusiasm; but all through the interminable narrative there ran a vein of impressive earnestness and sincerity which showed me plainly that, so far from his imagining that there was anything ridiculous or funny about his story, he regarded it as a really important matter, and admired its two heroes as men of transcendent genius in *finesse*. I let him go on in his own way, and never interrupted him once.

Reverend Leonidas W. H'm, Reverend Le—well, there was a feller here once by the name of *Jim* Smiley, in the winter of '49—or maybe it was the spring of '50—I don't recollect exactly, somehow, though what makes me think it was one or the other is because I remember the big flume warn't finished when he first come to the camp; but anyway, he was the curiousest man about always betting on anything that turned up you ever see, if he could get anybody to bet on the other side; and if he couldn't he'd change sides. Anyway that suited the other man would suit *him*—anyway just so's he got a bet,

257

he was satisfied. But still he was lucky, uncommon lucky; he most always come out winner. He was always ready and laying for a chance; there couldn't be no solit'ry thing mentioned but that feller'd offer to bet on it, and take ary side you please, as I was just telling you. If there was a horse-race, you'd find him flush or you'd find him busted at the end of it; if there was a dog-fight, he'd bet on it; if there was a cat-fight, he'd bet on it; if there was a chicken-fight, he'd bet on it; why, if there was two birds setting on a fence, he would bet you which one would fly first; or if there was a camp-meeting he would be there reg'lar to bet on Parson Walker which he judged to be the best exhorter about here, and so he was, too, and a good man. If he even see a straddle-bug start to go any where, he would bet how long it would take him to get to—to wherever he was going to, and if you took him up, he would foller that straddle-bug to Mexico but what he would find out where he was bound for and how long he was on the road. Lots of the boys here has seen that Smiley and can tell you about him. Why, it never made no difference to *him*—he'd bet on *anything*—the dangdest feller. Parson Walker's wife laid very sick once, for a good while, and it seemed as if they warn't going to save her; but one morning he come in, and Smiley up and asked him how she was, and he said she was considerable better—thank the Lord for His inf'nit mercy—and coming on so smart that with the blessing of Prov'dence she'd get well yet; and Smiley, before he thought, says, "Well, I'll resk two-and-a-half she don't anyway."

Thish-yer Smiley had a mare—the boys called her the fifteen-minute nag, but that was only in fun, you know, because of course she was faster than that—and he used to win money on that horse, for all she was slow and always had the asthma, or the distemper, or the consumption, or something of that kind. They used to give her two or three hundred yards' start, and then pass her under way; but always at the fag end of the race she'd get excited and desperate like, and come cavorting and straddling up, and scattering her legs around limber, sometimes in the air and sometimes out to one side among the fences, and kicking up m-o-r-e dust and raising m-o-r-e racket with her coughing and sneezing and blowing her nose—and *always* fetch up at the stand just about a neck ahead, as near as you could cipher it down.

And he had a little small bull-pup, that to look at him you'd think he warn't worth a cent but to set around and look ornery and lay for a chance to steal something. But as soon as money was up on him he was a different dog; his under-jaw'd begin to stick out like the fo'castle of a steamboat, and his teeth would uncover and shine like the furnaces. And a dog might tackle him and bully-rag him, and bite him, and throw him over his shoulder two or three times, and Andrew Jackson—which was the name of the pup—Andrew Jackson would never let on but what *he* was satisfied, and hadn't expected nothing else—and the bets being doubled and doubled on the other side all the time, till the money was all up; and then all of a sudden he would grab that other dog just by the j'int of his hind leg and freeze to it—not chaw, you understand, but only just grip and hang on till they throwed up the sponge, if it was a year. Smiley always come out winner on that pup, till he harnessed a dog once that didn't have no hind legs, because they'd been sawed off in a circular saw, and when the thing had gone along far enough, and the money was all up, and he come to make a snatch for his pet holt, he see in a minute how he'd been imposed on, and how the other dog had him in the door, so to speak, and he 'peared surprised, and then he looked sorter discouraged-like, and didn't try no more to win the fight, and so he got shucked out bad. He give Smiley a look, as much as to say his heart was broke, and it was *his* fault for putting up a dog that hadn't no hind legs for him to take holt of, which was his main dependence in a fight, and then he limped off a piece and laid down and died. It was a good pup, was that Andrew Jackson, and would have made a name for hisself if he'd lived, for the stuff was in him and he had genius—I know it, because he hadn't no opportunities to speak of, and it don't stand to reason that a dog could make such a fight as he could under them circumstances if he hadn't no talent. It always makes me feel sorry when I think of that last fight of his'n, and the way it turned out.

Well, thish-yer Smiley had rat-tarriers, and chicken cocks, and tom-cats, and all them kind of things till you couldn't rest, and you couldn't fetch nothing for him to bet on but he'd match you. He ketched a frog one day, and took him home, and said he cal'lated to educate him; and so he never done nothing for three months but set in his back yard and learn that frog to jump. And you bet you he *did* learn him, too. He'd give him a little punch behind, and the next minute you'd see that frog whirling in the air like a doughnut—see him turn one summerset, or maybe a couple, if he got a good start, and come down flat-footed and all right, like a cat. He got him up so in the matter of ketching flies, and kep' him in practice so constant, that he'd nail a fly every time as fur as he could see him. Smiley said all a frog wanted was education and he could do 'most anything—and I believe him. Why, I've seen him set Dan'l Webster down here on this floor—Dan'l Webster was the name of the frog—and sing out, "Flies, Dan'l, flies!" and quicker'n you could wink he'd spring straight up and snake a fly off'n the counter there, and flop down on the floor ag'in as solid as a gob of mud, and fall to scratching the side of his head with his hind foot as indifferent as if he hadn't no idea he'd been doin' any more'n any frog might do. You never see a frog so modest and straightfor'ard as he was, for all he was so gifted. And when it come to fair and square jumping on a dead level, he could get over more ground at one straddle than any animal of his breed you ever see. Jumping on a dead level was his strong suit, you understand; and when it come to that, Smiley would ante up money on him as long as he had a red. Smiley was monstrous proud of his frog, and well he might be, for fellers that had traveled and been everywhere? all said he laid over any frog that ever *they* see.

Well, Smiley kep' the beast in a little lattice box, and he used to fetch him down-town sometimes and lay for a bet. One day a feller—a stranger in the camp, he was—come acrost him with his box, and says:

"What might it be that you've got in the box?"

And Smiley says, sorter indifferent-like, "It might be a parrot, or it might be a canary, maybe, but it ain't—it's only just a frog."

And the feller took it, and looked at it careful, and turned it round this way and that, and says, "H'm—so 'tis. Well, what's *he* good for?"

"Well," Smiley says, easy and careless, "he's good enough for *one* thing, I should judge—he can outjump any frog in Calaveras County."

The feller took the box again, and took another long, particular look, and give it back to Smiley,

and says, very deliberate, "Well," he says, "I don't
see no p'ints about that frog that's any better'n ary
other frog."

"Maybe you don't," Smiley says. "Maybe you
understand frogs and maybe you don't understand
'em; maybe you've had experience, and maybe you
ain't only a amature, as it were. Anyways, I've got
my opinion, and I'll resk forty dollars that he can
outjump any frog in Calaveras County."

And the feller studied a minute, and then says,
kinder sad like, "Well, I'm only a stranger here,
and I ain't got no frog; but if I had a frog I'd bet
you."

And then Smiley says, "That's all right—that's
all right—if you'll hold my box a minute I'll go and
get you a frog." And so the feller took the box,
and put up his forty dollars along with Smiley's,
and set down to wait.

So he set there a good while thinking and thinking to himself, and then he got the frog out and
prized his mouth open and took a teaspoon and
filled him full of quail shot—filled him pretty near
up to his chin—and set him on the floor. Smiley he
went to the swamp and slopped around in the mud
for a long time, and finally he ketched a frog, and
fetched him in, and give him to this feller, and says:

"Now, if you're ready, set him alongside of
Dan'l, with his forepaws just even with Dan'l's, and
I'll give the word." Then he says, "One—two—
three—*git!*" and him and the feller touched up
the frogs from behind, and the new frog hopped
off lively, but Dan'l give a heave, and hysted up
his shoulders—so—like a Frenchman, but it warn't
no use—he couldn't budge; he was planted as solid
as a church, and he couldn't no more stir than if he
was anchored out. Smiley was a good deal surprised, and he was disgusted, too, but he didn't
have no idea what the matter was, of course.

The feller took the money and started away; and when he was going out at the door, he sorter jerked his thumb over his shoulder—so—at Dan'l, and says again, very deliberate, "Well," he says, "*I* don't see no p'ints about that frog that's any better'n any other frog."

Smiley he stood scratching his head and looking down at Dan'l a long time, and at last he says, "I do wonder what in the nation that frog throw'd off for—I wonder if there ain't something the matter with him—he 'pears to look mighty baggy, somehow." And he ketched Dan'l by the nap of the neck and hefted him, and says, "Why, blame my cats, if he don't weigh five pound!" and turned him upside down and he belched out a double handful of shot. And then he see how it was, and he was the maddest man—he set the frog down and took out after that feller, but he never ketched him. And——

[Here Simon Wheeler heard his name called from the front yard, and got up to see what was wanted.] And turning to me as he moved away, he said: "Jest set where you are, stranger, and rest easy—I ain't going to be gone a second."

But, by your leave, I did not think that a continuation of the history of the enterprising vagabond *Jim* Smiley would be likely to afford me much information concerning the Reverend *Leonidas W.* Smiley, and so I started away.

At the door I met the sociable Wheeler returning, and he buttonholed me and recommenced:

"Well, thish-yer Smiley had a yaller, one-eyed cow that didn't have no tail, only just a short stump like a bannanner, and——"

However, lacking both time and inclination, I did not wait to hear about the afflicted cow, but took my leave.

263

JOHN WESLEY

JOHN WESLEY, born in Lincolnshire, Eng., 1703; died 1791. His education was obtained at Oxford. He has gone into history as the founder of Methodism. During the 65 years of his ministry he traveled 270,000 miles and preached over 40,000 sermons. His life was one of the most strenuous in the history of the Christian church.

THE DOCTRINE OF PREDESTINATION

THOUGH you use softer words than some, you mean the selfsame thing: and God's decree concerning the Election of Grace, according to your account of it, amounts to neither more nor less than what others call "God's Decree of Reprobation." Call it therefore by what name you please— Election, Pretermission, Predestination, or Reprobation—it comes in the end to the same thing. The sense of all is plainly this: By virtue of an eternal, unchangeable, irresistible decree of God, one part of mankind are infalliby saved, and the rest infallibly damned; it being impossible that any of the former should be damned, or that any of the latter should be saved. . . .

This doctrine is full of blasphemy, for it represents our blessed Lord as a hyprocrite and dissembler in saying one thing and meaning another; in pretending a love which He has not. It also repre-
· ·ts the most Holy God as more false, more cruel,

and more unjust than the Devil: for in point of fact it says that God has condemned millions of souls to everlasting fire for continuing in sin which, for want of grace He gives them not, they are unable to avoid. . . .

This is the blasphemy clearly contained in the horrible decree of Predestination. And here I fix my foot. On this I join issue with every asserter of it. You represent God as worse than the Devil. But you say you will prove it by Scripture. Hold! What will you prove by Scripture? That God is worse than the Devil? It cannot be. Whatever the Scripture proves, it can never prove this. Whatever its true meaning may be, this cannot be its true meaning. Do you ask, "What is its true meaning, then?" If I say, "I know not," you have gained nothing; for there are many Scriptures the true sense whereof neither you nor I shall know till death is swallowed up in victory.

DIVINE LOVE

(From the German of Gerhard Tersteegen)

THOU hidden Love of God! whose height,
  Whose depth unfathomed, no man knows,
I see from far Thy beauteous light,
  Only I sigh for Thy repose.
My heart is pained, nor can it be
At rest till it finds rest in Thee.

Thy secret voice invites me still
  The sweetness of Thy yoke to prove;
And fain I would; but though my will
  Seem fixed, yet wide my passions rove,
Yet hindrances strew all the way;
I aim at Thee yet from Thee stray.

'Tis mercy all, that Thou hast brought
  My mind to seek her peace in Thee!
Yet while I seek, but find Thee not,
  No peace my wandering soul shall see.
Oh, when shall all my wanderings end,
And all my steps to Theeward tend?

Is there a thing beneath the sun
  That strives with Thee my heart to share?
Ah, tear it thence, and reign alone,
  The Lord of every motion there!
Then shall my heart from earth be free,
When it hath found repose in Thee.

Oh, hide this self from me, that I
  No more—but Christ in me—may live!
My vile affections crucify,
  Nor let one darling lust survive!
In all things nothing may I see,
Nothing desire or seek but Thee!

O Love! Thy sovereign aid impart
  To save me from low-thoughted care;
Chase this self-will through all my heart,
  Through all its latent mazes there;
Make me Thy duteous child, that I
Ceaseless may " Abba, Father," cry.

Ah, no! ne'er will I backward turn—
  Thine, wholly Thine, alone I am;
Thrice happy he who views with scorn
  Earth's toys, for Thee his constant flame.
Oh, help, that I may never move
From the blest footsteps of Thy love!

Each moment draw from earth away
  My heart, that lowly waits thy call;
Speak to my inmost soul, and say,
  " I am thy Love, thy God, thy All!"
To feel Thy power, to hear Thy voice,
To taste Thy love, be all my choice.

COMMIT THOU ALL THY GRIEFS

(From the German of Paul Gerhardt)

COMMIT thou all thy griefs
    And ways into his hands,
To his sure truth and tender care,
    Who earth and heaven commands;

Who points the clouds their course,
    Whom winds and seas obey,
He shall direct thy wandering feet,
    He shall prepare thy way.

*   *   *   *   *

Give to the winds thy fears;
    Hope, and be undismayed;
God hears thy sighs, and counts thy tears,
    God shall lift up thy head.

Through waves and clouds and storms,
    He gently clears thy way;
Wait thou his time; so shall this night
    Soon end in joyous day.

Still heavy is thy heart?
    Still sink thy spirits down?
Cast off the weight, let fear depart,
    And every care be gone.

What though thou rulest not?
    Yet heaven and earth and hell
Proclaim, God sitteth on the Throne,
    And ruleth all things well!

    Leave to his sovereign sway
    To choose and to command;
So shalt thou wondering own, his way
    How wise, how strong his hand!

    Far, far above thy thought
    His counsel shall appear,
When fully he the work hath wrought
    That caused thy needless fear.

    Thou seest our weakness, Lord!
    Our hearts are known to thee:
Oh! lift thou up the sinking hand,
    Confirm the feeble knee!

    Let us, in life, in death,
    Thy steadfast Truth declare,
And publish, with our latest breath,
    Thy love and guardian care!

WALT WHITMAN

WALT WHITMAN, an America poet, born in West Hills, Long Island, N. Y., in 1819; died in Camden, N. J., in 1892. He was in turn printer, carpenter, teacher and journalist. He served in the Hospital Corps, in the Civil War, and later was a government clerk. His first volume of poems of importance, "Leaves of Grass," was published in 1855 and it always ranked among his best. Among his later productions were: "November Boughs," "Sands at Seventy" and "Good-bye, My Fancy."

TO THE MAN-OF-WAR-BIRD

(Copyright by Small, Maynard & Co.)

THOU who hast slept all night upon the storm,
    Waking renewed on thy prodigious pinions,
(Burst the wild storm? above it thou ascended'st,
And rested on the sky, thy slave that cradled thee,)
Now a blue point, far, far in heaven floating,
As to the light emerging here on deck I watch thee,
(Myself a speck, a point on the world's floating
    vast).
Far, far at sea,
After the night's fierce drifts have strewn the shore
    with wrecks,
With re-appearing day as now so happy and serene,
The rosy and elastic dawn, the flashing sun,
The limped spread of air cerulean,
Thou also re-appearest.
Thou born to match the gale (thou art all wings),
To cope with heaven and earth and sea and hurri-
    cane,
Thou ship of air that never furl'st thy sails,

Days, even weeks untired and onward, through
   spaces, realms gyrating,
At dusk thou look'st on Senegal, at morn America,
That sport'st amid the lightning-flash and thunder-
   cloud,
In them, in thy experiences, had'st thou my soul,
What joys! what joys were thine!

IMMORTALITY

WHOEVER you are! you are he or she for
   whom the earth is solid and liquid;
You are he or she for whom the sun and the moon
   hang in the sky;
For none more than you are the present and the
   past;
For none more than you is immortality!
Each man to himself, and each woman to herself,
   is the word of the past and present, and the
   word of immortality:
No one can acquire for another—not one!
No one can grow for another—not one!

I HEAR AMERICA SINGING

I HEAR America singing, the varied carols I
   hear,
Those of mechanic singing his as it should be,
   blithe and strong,
The carpenter singing his as he measures his plank
   or beam,
The mason singing his as he makes ready for work,
   or leaves off work,
The boatman singing what belongs to him in his
   boat, the deck-hand singing on the steam-boat
   deck,

The shoemaker singing as he sits on his bench, the
    hatter singing as he stands,
The wood-cutter's song, the plowboy's on his way
    in the morning, or at noon intermission or at
    sun-down,
The delicious singing of the mother, or of the young
    wife at work, or of the girl sewing or washing,
Each singing what belongs to him or her and to
    none else,
The day what belongs to the day—at night the party
    of young fellows, robust, friendly,
Singing with melodious mouths their strong, melo-
    dious songs.

O CAPTAIN! MY CAPTAIN!

(Copyright by Small, Maynard & Co.)

O CAPTAIN! my Captain! our fearful trip is
    done;
The ship has weathered every rack, the prize we
    sought is won;
The port is near, the bells I hear, the people all
    exulting,
While follow eyes the steady keel, the vessel grim
    and daring.
      But O heart! heart! heart!
        O the bleeding drops of red,
          Where on the deck my Captain lies,
          Fallen cold and dead.

O Captain! my Captain! rise up and hear the bells:
Rise up!—for you the flag is flung—for you the
    bugle trills,
For you bouquets and ribboned wreaths—for you
    the shores a-crowding;
For you they call, the swaying mass, their eager
    faces turning.

Hear Captain! dear father!
  This arm beneath your head!
    It is some dream that on the deck
      You've fallen cold and dead.

My Captain does not answer, his lips are pale and
    still;
My father does not feel my arm, he has nor pulse
    nor will;
The ship is anchored safe and sound, its voyage
    closed and done,
From fearful trip the victor ship comes in with ob-
    ject won:
    Exult O shores, and ring O bells!
      But I with mournful tread,
        Walk the deck my Captain lies,
          Fallen cold and dead.

HUSHED BE THE CAMPS TO-DAY

(Copyright by Small, Maynard & Co.)

(May 4th, 1865)

HUSHED be the camps to-day,
    And soldiers, let us drape our war-worn
      weapons,
And each with musing soul retire to celebrate
Our dear commander's death.

No more for him life's stormy conflicts,
Nor victory, nor defeat;—no more time's dark
    events,
Charging like ceaseless clouds across the sky.

But sing, poet, in our name,
Sing of the love we bore him—because you, dweller
    in camps, know it truly.

As they invault the coffin there,
Sing—as they close the doors of earth upon him—
    one verse,
For the heavy hearts of soldiers.

JOHN G. WHITTIER

(Houghton, Mifflin & Co., Publishers)

JOHN GREENLEAF WHITTIER, born in Haverhill, Mass., 1807; died in Hampton Falls, N. H., in 1892. He is known as the Quaker poet. His pen gained skill in journalism. At one time he was editor of the *American Manufacturer* in Boston, and at another of the *New England Weekly Review* of Hartford. Then he edited the *Pennsylvania Freeman* of Philadelphia, which a mob destroyed. From this time until 1863 he was one of the most prominent anti-slavery men in the country. Much of his earlier poetry was inspired by his sympathy for the enslaved. In fact, most of his poetry originated in current events, and revealed the patriotic and humane spirit of the author. His literary work is of the kind whose popularity is unlikely to grow dim with time.

THE SLAVE-SHIPS

"That fatal, that perfidious bark,
Built i' the eclipse, and rigged with curses dark."
—*Milton's Lycidas.*

ALL ready?" cried the captain;
"Ay, ay!" the seamen said;
"Heave up the worthless lubbers,—
The dying and the dead."
Up from the slave-ship's prison
Fierce, bearded heads were thrust:
"Now let the sharks look to it,—
Toss up the dead ones first!"

Corpse after corpse came up,—
　Death had been busy there;
Where every blow is mercy,
　Why should the spoiler spare?
Corpse after corpse they cast
　Sullenly from the ship,
Yet bloody with the traces
　Of fetter-link and whip.

Gloomily stood the captain,
　With his arms upon his breast,
With his cold brow sternly knotted,
　And his iron lip compressed.
" Are all the dead dogs over ? "
　Growled through that matted lip,—
" The blind ones are no better,
　Let's lighten the good ship."

Hark ! from the ship's dark bosom,
　The very sounds of hell !
The ringing clank of iron,—
　The maniac's short, sharp yell !—
The hoarse, low curse, throat-stilled,—
　The starving infant's moan,—
The horror of a breaking heart
　Poured through a mother's groan.

Up from that loathsome prison
　The stricken blind ones came:
Below, had all been darkness,—
　Above, was still the same.
Yet the holy breath of heaven
　Was sweetly breathing there,
And the heated brow of fever
　Cooled in the soft sea air.

"Overboard with them, shipmates!"
  Cutlass and dirk were plied;
Fettered and blind, one after one,
  Plunged down the vessel's side.
The saber smote above,—
  Beneath, the lean shark lay,
Waiting with wide and bloody jaw
  His quick and human prey.

God of the earth! what cries
  Rang upward unto thee?
Voices of agony and blood,
  From ship-deck and from sea.
The last dull plunge was heard,—
  The last wave caught its stain,—
And the unsated shark looked up
  For human hearts in vain.

*   *   *   *   *

Red glowed the western waters,—
  The setting sun was there,
Scattering alike on wave and cloud
  His fiery mesh of hair.
Amidst a group in blindness,
  A solitary eye
Gazed, from the burdened slaver's deck,
  Into that burning sky.

"A storm," spoke out the gazer,
  "Is gathering and at hand,—
Curse on 't—I 'd give my other eye
  For one firm rood of land."
And then he laughed,—but only
  His echoed laugh replied,—
For the blinded and the suffering
  Alone were at his side.

Night settled on the waters,
　　And on a stormy heaven,
While fiercely on that lone ship's track
　　The thunder-gust was driven.
" A sail!—thank God, a sail ! "
　　And as the helmsman spoke,
Up through the stormy murmur
　　A shout of gladness broke.

Down came the stranger vessel,
　　Unheeding on her way,
So near, that on the slaver's deck
　　Fell off her driven spray.
" Ho! for the love of mercy,—
　　We 're perishing and blind! "
A wail of utter agony
　　Came back upon the wind:

" Help *us!* for we are stricken
　　With blindness every one;
Ten days we 've floated fearfully,
　　Unnoting star or sun.
Our ship's the slaver Leon,—
　　We 've but a score on board,—
Our slaves are all gone over,—
　　Help,—for the love of God ! "

On livid brows of agony
　　The broad red lightning shone,—
But the roar of wind and thunder
　　Stifled the answering groan
Wailed from the broken waters
　　A last despairing cry,
As, kindling in the stormy light,
　　The stranger ship went by.

*　　　*　　　*　　　*　　　*

In the sunny Guadaloupe
  A dark-hulled vessel lay,—
With a crew who noted never
  The nightfall or the day.
The blossom of the orange,
  Was white by every stream,
And tropic leaf, and flower, and bird
  Were in the warm sunbeam.

And the sky was bright as ever,
  And the moonlight slept as well,
On the palm-trees by the hillside,
  And the streamlet of the dell:
And the glances of the Creole
  Were still as archly deep,
And her smiles as full as ever
  Of passion and of sleep.

But vain were bird and blossom,
  The green earth and the sky,
And the smile of human faces,
  To the slaver's darkened eye;
At the breaking of the morning,
  At the star-lit evening time,
O'er a world of light and beauty
  Fell the blackness of his crime.

THE MERRIMACK

["The Indians speak of a beautiful river, far to
the south, which they call Merrimack."—Sieur de
Monts: 1604]

STREAM of my fathers! sweetly still
  The sunset rays thy valley fill;
Poured slantwise down the long defile,
Wave, wood, and spire beneath them smile.

I see the winding Powow fold
The green hill in its belt of gold,
And following down its wavy line,
Its sparkling waters blend with thine.
There 's not a tree upon thy side,
Nor rock, which thy returning tide
As yet hath left abrupt and stark
Above thy evening water-mark;
No calm cove with its rocky hem,
No isle whose emerald swells begem
Thy broad, smooth current; not a sail
Bowed to the freshening ocean gale;
No small boat with its busy oars,
Nor gray wall sloping to thy shores;
Nor farm-house with its maple shade,
Or rigid poplar colonnade,
But lies distinct and full in sight,
Beneath this gush of sunset light.
Centuries ago, that harbor-bar,
Stretching its length of foam afar,
And Salisbury's beach of shining sand,
And yonder island's wave-smoothed strand,
Saw the adventurer's tiny sail
Flit, stooping from the eastern gale;
And o'er these woods and waters broke
The cheer from Britain's hearts of oak,
As brightly on the voyager's eye,
Weary of forest, sea, and sky,
Breaking the dull continuous wood,
The Merrimack rolled down his flood;
Mingling that clear pellucid brook,
Which channels vast Agioochook
When spring-time's sun and shower unlock
The frozen fountains of the rock,
And more abundant waters given
From that pure lake, "The Smile f Heaven,"
Tributes from vale and mountain-side,—
With ocean's dark, eternal tide!

On yonder rocky cape, which braves
The stormy challenge of the waves,
Midst tangled vine and dwarfish wood,
The hardy Anglo-Saxon stood,
Planting upon the topmost crag
The staff of England's battle-flag;
And, while from out its heavy fold
Saint George's crimson cross unrolled,
Midst roll of drum and trumpet blare,
And weapons brandishing in air,
He gave to that lone promotory
The sweetest name in all his story;
Of her, the flower of Islam's daughters,
Whose harems look on Stamboul's waters,—
Who, when the chance of war had bound
The Moslem chain his limbs around,
Wreathed o'er with silk that iron chain,
Soothed with her smiles his hours of pain,
And fondly to her youthful slave
A dearer gift than freedom gave.

But look!—the yellow light no more
Streams down on wave and verdant shore;
And clearly on the calm air swells
The twilight voice of distant bells.
From Ocean's bosom, white and thin,
The mists come slowly rolling in;
Hills, woods, the river's rocky rim,
Amidst the sea-like vapor swim,
While yonder lonely coast-light, set
Within its wave-washed minaret,
Half quenched, a beamless star and pale,
Shines dimly through its cloudy veil!

Home of my fathers!—I have stood
Where Hudson rolled his lordly flood:
Seen sunrise rest and sunset fade
Along his frowning Palisade;

Looked down the Apalachian peak
On Juniata's silver streak;
Have seen along his valley gleam
The Mohawk's softly winding stream;
The level light of sunset shine
Through broad Potomac's hem of pine;
And autumn's rainbow-tinted banner
Hang lightly o'er the Susquehanna;
Yet, whereso'er his step might be,
Thy wandering child looked back to thee!
Heard in his dreams thy river's sound
Of murmuring on its pebbly bound,
The unforgotten swell and roar
Of waves on thy familiar shore;
And saw, amidst the curtained gloom
And quiet of his lonely room,
Thy sunset scenes before him pass;
As, in Agrippa's magic glass,
The loved and lost arose to view,
Remembered groves in greenness grew,
Bathed still in childhood's morning dew,
Along whose bowers of beauty swept
Whatever Memory's mourners wept,
Sweet faces, which the charnel kept,
Young, gentle eyes, which long had slept;
And while the gazer leaned to trace,
More near, some dear familiar face,
He wept to find the vision flown,—
A phantom and a dream alone!

MY SOUL AND I

STAND still, my soul, in the silent dark
I would question thee,
Alone in the shadow drear and stark
    With God and me!

MY SOUL AND I

What, my soul, was thy errand here?
    Was it mirth or ease,
Or heaping up dust from year to year?
    "Nay, none of these!"

Speak, soul, aright in His holy sight
    Whose eye looks still
And steadily on thee through the night:
    "To do his will!"

What hast thou done, O soul of mine,
    That thou tremblest so?—
Hast thou wrought his task, and kept the line
    He bade thee go?

What, silent all!—art sad of cheer?
    Art fearful now?
When God seemed far and men were near
    How brave wert thou!

Aha! thou tremblest!—well I see
    Thou 'rt craven grown.
Is it so hard with God and me
    To stand alone?—

Summon thy sunshine bravery back,
    Oh wretched sprite!
Let me hear thy voice through this deep and black
    Abysmal night.

What hast thou wrought for Right and Truth,
    For God and man,
From the golden hours of bright-eyed youth
    To life's mid span?

281

Ah, soul of mine, thy tones I hear,
  But weak and low,
Like far sad murmurs on my ear
  They come and go.

"I have wrestled stoutly with the Wrong,
  And borne the Right
From beneath the footfall of the throng
  To life and light.

"Wherever Freedom shivered a chain,
  God speed, quoth I;
To Error amidst her shouting train
  I gave the lie."

Ah, soul of mine! ah, soul of mine!
  Thy deeds are well:
Were they wrought for Truth's sake or for thine?
  My soul, pray tell.

"Of all the work my hand hath wrought
  Beneath the sky,
Save a place in kindly human thought,
  No gain have I."

Go to, go to!—for thy very self
  Thy deeds were done:
Thou for fame, the miser for pelf,
  Your end is one!

And where art thou going, soul of mine?
  Canst see the end?
And whither this troubled life of thine
  Evermore doth tend?

282

What daunts thee now?—what shakes thee so?
    My sad soul say.
"I see a cloud like a curtain low
    Hang o'er my way.

"Whither I go I cannot tell:
    That cloud hangs black,
High as the heaven and deep as hell
    Across my track.

"I see its shadow coldly enwrap
    The souls before.
Sadly they enter it, step by step,
    To return no more.

"They shrink, they shudder, dear God! they kneel
    To thee in prayer.
They shut their eyes on the cloud, but feel
    That it still is there.

"In vain they turn from the dread Before
    To the Known and Gone;
For while gazing behind them evermore
    Their feet glide on.

"Yet, at times, I see upon sweet pale faces
    A light begin
To tremble, as if from holy places
    And shrines within.

"And at times methinks their cold lips move
    With hymn and prayer,
As if somewhat of awe, but more of love
    And hope were there.

"I call on the souls who have left the light
    To reveal their lot;
I bend mine ear to that wall of night,
    And they answer not.

"But I hear around me sighs of pain
    And the cry of fear,
And a sound like the slow sad dropping of rain,
    Each drop a tear!

"Ah, the cloud is dark, and day by day
    I am moving thither:
I must pass beneath it on my way—
    God pity me!—WHITHER?"

Ah, soul of mine! so brave and wise
    In the life-storm loud,
Fronting so calmly all human eyes
    In the sunlit crowd!

Now standing apart with God and me
    Thou art weakness all,
Gazing vainly after the things to be
    Through Death's dread wall.

But never for this, never for this
    Was thy being lent;
For the craven's fear is but selfishness,
    Like his merriment.

Folly and Fear are sisters twain:
    One closing here eyes,
The other peopling the dark inane
    With spectral lies.

Know well, my soul, God's hand controls
    Whate'er thou fearest;
Round him in calmest music rolls
    Whate'er thou hearest.

What to thee is shadow, to him is day,
    And the end he knoweth,
And not on a blind and aimless way
    The spirit goeth.

Man sees no future,—a phantom show
    Is alone before him:
Past Time is dead, and the grasses grow,
    And flowers bloom o'er him.

Nothing before, nothing behind;
    The steps of Faith
Fall on the seeming void, and find
    The rock beneath.

The Present, the Present is all thou hast
    For thy sure possessing;
Like the patriarch's angel hold it fast
    Till it gives its blessing.

Why fear the night? why shrink from Death,
    That phantom wan?
There is nothing in heaven or earth beneath
    Save God and man.

Peopling the shadows we turn from Him
    And from one another;
All is spectral and vague and dim
    Save God and our brother!

Like warp and woof all destinies
    Are woven fast,
Linked in sympathy like the keys
    Of an organ vast.

Pluck one thread, and the web ye mar;
    Break but one
Of a thousand keys, and the paining jar
    Through all will run.

O restless spirit! wherefore strain
    Beyond thy sphere?
Heaven and hell, with their joy and pain,
    Are now and here.

Back to thyself is measured well
    All thou hast given;
Thy neighbor's wrong is thy present hell,
    His bliss, thy heaven.

And in life, in death, in dark and light,
    All are in God's care;
Sound the black abyss, pierce the deep of night,
    And he is there!

All which is real now remaineth,
    And fadeth never:
The hand which upholds it now sustaineth
    The soul forever.

Leaning on him, make with reverent meekness
    His own thy will,
And with strength from Him shall thy utter weak-
    ness
    Life's task fulfil;

And that cloud itself, which now before thee
    Lies dark in view,
Shall with beams of light from the inner glory
    Be stricken through.

And like meadow mist through autumn's dawn
    Uprolling thin,
Its thickest folds when about thee drawn
    Let sunlight in.

Then of what is to be, and of what is done,
    Why queriest thou?—
The past and the time to be are one,
    And both are now!

MAUD MULLER

MAUD MULLER, on a summer's day,
    Raked the meadow sweet with hay.

Beneath her torn hat glowed the wealth
Of simple beauty and rustic health.

Singing, she wrought, and her merry glee
The mocking-bird echoed from his tree.

But when she glanced to the far-off town,
White from its hill-slope looking down,

The sweet song died, and a vague unrest
And a nameless longing filled her breast,—

A wish, that she hardly dared to own,
For something better than she had known.

The Judge rode slowly down the lane,
Smoothing his horse's chestnut mane.

He drew his bridle in the shade
Of the apple-trees, to greet the maid,

And ask a draught from the spring that flowed
Through the meadow across the road.

She stooped where the cool spring bubbled up,
And filled for him her small tin cup,

And blushed as she gave it, looking down
On her feet so bare, and her tattered gown.

"Thanks !" said the Judge; "a sweeter draught
From a fairer hand was never quaffed."

He spoke of the grass and flowers and trees,
Of the singing birds and the humming bees;

Then talked of the haying, and wondered whether
The cloud in the west would bring foul weather.

And Maud forgot her brier-torn gown,
And her graceful ankles bare and brown;

And listened, while a pleased surprise
Looked from her long-lashed hazel eyes.

At last, like one who for delay
Seeks a vain excuse, he rode away.

Maud Muller looked and sighed: "Ah me!
That I the Judge's bride might be!

"He would dress me up in silks so fine,
And praise and toast me at his wine.

"My father should wear a broadcloth coat;
My brother should sail a painted boat.

I 'd dress my mother so grand and gay,
And the baby should have a new toy each day.

And I 'd feed the hungry and clothe the poor,
And all should bless me who left our door."

The Judge looked back as he climbed the hill,
And saw Maud Muller standing still.

A form more fair, a face more sweet,
Ne'er hath it been my lot to meet.

And her modest answer and graceful air
Show her wise and good as she is fair.

Would she were mine, and I to-day,
Like her, a harvester of hay:

No doubtful balance of rights and wrongs,
Nor weary lawyers with endless tongues,

But low of cattle and song of birds,
And health and quiet and loving words."

But he thought of his sisters proud and cold,
And his mother vain of her rank and gold.

So, closing his heart, the Judge rode on,
And Maud was left in the field alone.

But the lawyers smiled that afternoon,
When he hummed in court an old love-tune;

And the young girl mused beside the well,
Till the rain on the unraked clover fell.

He wedded a wife of richest dower
Who lived for fashion, as he for power.

Yet oft, in his marble hearth's bright glow,
He watched a picture come and go;

And sweet Maud Muller's hazel eyes
Looked out in their innocent surprise.

Oft, when the wine in his glass was red,
He longed for the wayside well instead;

And closed his eyes on his garnished rooms,
To dream of meadows and clover-blooms.

And the proud man sighed, with a secret pain,
" Ah, that I were free again!

" Free as when I rode that day,
Where the barefoot maiden raked her hay."

She wedded a man unlearned and poor,
And many children played round her door.

But care and sorrow, and childbirth pain,
Left their traces on heart and brain.

And oft, when the summer sun shone hot
On the new-mown hay in the meadow lot,

And she heard the little spring brook fall
Over the roadside, through the wall.

In the shade of the apple-tree again
She saw a rider draw his rein.

And, gazing down with timid grace,
She felt his pleased eyes read her face.

Sometimes her narrow kitchen walls
Stretched away into stately halls;

he weary wheel to a spinnet turned,
he tallow candle an astral burned,

nd for him who sat by the chimney lug,
ozing and grumbling o'er pipe and mug,

. manly form at her side she saw,
nd joy was duty and love was law.

hen she took up her burden of life again,
aying only, " It might have been."

las for maiden, alas for Judge,
or rich repiner and household drudge!

od pity them both! and pity us all,
Who vainly the dreams of youth recall.

or of all sad words of tongue or pen,
he saddest are these: " It might have been !"

h, well! for us all some sweet hope lies
eeply buried from human eyes;

nd, in the hereafter, angels may
oll the stone from its grave away!

THE BAREFOOT BOY

BLESSINGS on thee, little man,
  Barefoot boy, with cheek of tan!
With thy turned-up pantaloons,
And thy merry whistled tunes;
With thy red lip, redder still
Kissed by strawberries on the hill;
With the sunshine on thy face,
Through thy torn brim's jaunty grace;

From my heart I give thee joy,—
I was once a barefoot boy!
Prince thou art,—the grown-up man
Only is republican.
Let the million-dollared ride!
Barefoot, trudging at his side,
Thou hast more than he can buy
In the reach of ear and eye,—
Outward sunshine, inward joy:
Blessings on thee, barefoot boy!

O for boyhood's painless play,
Sleep that wakes in laughing day,
Health that mocks the doctor's rules,
Knowledge never learned of schools,
Of the wild bee's morning chase,
Of the wild-flower's time and place,
Flight of fowl and habitude
Of the tenants of the wood;
How the tortoise bears his shell,
How the woodchuck digs his cell,
And the ground-mole sinks his well;
How the robin feeds her young,
How the oriole's nest is hung;
Where the whitest lilies blow,
Where the freshest berries grow,
Where the groundnut trails its vine,
Where the wood-grape's clusters shine:
Of the black wasp's cunning way,
Mason of his walls of clay,
And the architectural plans
Of gray hornet artisans!—
For, eschewing books and tasks,
Nature answers all he asks;
Hand in hand with her he walks,
Face to face with her he talks,
Part and parcel of her joy,—
Blessings on the barefoot boy!

O for boyhood's time of June,
Crowding years in one brief moon,
When all things I heard or saw,
Me, their master, waited for.
I was rich in flowers and trees,
Humming-birds and honey-bees;
For my sport the squirrel played,
Plied the snouted mole his spade;
For my taste the blackberry cone
Purpled over hedge and stone;
Laughed the brook for my delight
Through the day and through the night.
Whispering at the garden wall,
Talked with me from fall to fall;
Mine the sand-rimmed pickerel pond,
Mine the walnut slopes beyond,
Mine, on bending orchard trees,
Apples of Hesperides!
Still as my horizon grew,
Larger grew my riches too;
All the world I saw or knew
Seemed a complex Chinese toy,
Fashioned for a barefoot boy!

O for festal dainties spread,
Like my bowl of milk and bread,—
Pewter spoon and bowl of wood,
On the door-stone, gray and rude!
O'er me, like a regal tent,
Cloudy-ribbed, the sunset bent,
Purple-curtained, fringed with gold,
Looped in many a wind-swung fold;
While for music came the play
Of the pied frogs' orchestra;
And, to light the noisy choir,
Lit the fly his lamp of fire.
I was monarch: pomp and joy
Waited on the barefoot boy!

Cheerily, then, my little man,
Live and laugh, as boyhood can!
Though the flinty slopes be hard,
Stubble-speared the new-mown sward,
Every morn shall lead thee through
Fresh baptisms of the dew;
Every evening from thy feet
Shall the cool wind kiss the heat:
All too soon these feet must hide
In the prison cells of pride,
Lose the freedom of the sod,
Like a colt's for work be shod,
Made to tread the mills of toil,
Up and down in ceaseless moil:
Happy if their track be found
Never on forbidden ground;
Happy if they sink not in
Quick and treacherous sands of sin.
Ah! that thou couldst know thy joy,
Ere it passes, barefoot boy!

NATHANIEL P. WILLIS

NATHANIEL PARKER WILLIS, an American poet, was born in Portland, Maine, in 1806; died at Idlewild-on-the-Hudson in 1867. He went early to Europe and contributed to the New York *Mirror* an account of his travels. He later founded a paper in New York City, but gave it up to enter the diplomatic service in Berlin. The *Home Journal* was founded by him on his return. His lyrics are highly polished, and possess a distinctive charm. He was a seeker after dramatic effects, and was usually successful, but he was not a poet of the first rank.

ABSALOM

THE waters slept. Night's silvery veil hung low
 On Jordan's bosom, and the eddies curled
Their glassy rings beneath it, like the still,
Unbroken beating of the sleeper's pulse.
The reeds bent down the stream; the willow leaves,
With a soft cheek upon the lulling tide,
Forgot the lifting winds; and the long stems,
Whose flowers the water, like a gentle nurse,
Bears on its bosom, quietly gave way,
And leaned in graceful attitudes to rest.
How strikingly the course of nature tells,
By its light heed of human suffering,
That it was fashioned for a happier world!
 King David's limbs were weary. He had fled
From far Jerusalem; and now he stood,
With his faint people, for a little rest,
Upon the shore of Jordan. The light wind
Of morn was stirring, and he bared his brow
To its refreshing breath; for he had worn

The mourner's covering, and he had not felt
That he could see his people until now.
They gathered round him on the fresh green bank,
And spoke their kindly words; and, as the sun
Rose up in heaven, he knelt among them there,
And bowed his head upon his hands to pray.
Oh! when the heart is full,—when bitter thoughts
Come crowding thickly up for utterance,
And the poor common words of courtesy
Are such an empty mockery,—how much
The bursting heart may pour itself in prayer!
He prayed for Israel; and his voice went up
Strongly and fervently. He prayed for those
Whose love had been his shield; and his deep tones
Grew tremulous. But, oh! for Absalom,—
For his estranged, misguided Absalom,—
The proud, bright being who had burst away
In all his princely beauty, to defy
The heart that cherished him,—for him he poured,
In agony that would not be controlled,
Strong supplication, and forgave him there,
Before his God, for his deep sinfulness.

*   *   *   *   *   *   *

The pall was settled. He who slept beneath
Was straightened for the grave; and, as the folds
Sunk to the still proportions, they betrayed
The matchless symmetry of Absalom.
His hair was yet unshorn, and silken curls
Were floating round the tassels as they swayed
To the admitted air, as glossy now
As when, in hours of gentle dalliance, bathing
The snowy fingers of Judea's daughters.
His helm was at his feet; his banner, soiled
With trailing through Jerusalem, was laid,
Reversed, beside him; and the jeweled hilt,
Whose diamonds lit the passage of his blade,
Rested, like mockery, on his covered brow.

ABSALOM

The soldiers of the king trod to and fro,
Clad in the garb of battle; and their chief,
The mighty Joab, stood beside the bier,
And gazed upon the dark pall steadfastly,
As if he feared the slumberer might stir.
A slow step startled him. He grasped his blade
As if a trumpet rang; but the bent form
Of David entered, and he gave command,
In a low tone, to his few followers,
And left him with his dead. The king stood still
Till the last echo died; then, throwing off
The sackcloth from his brow, and laying back
The pall from the still features of his child,
He bowed his head upon him, and broke forth
In the resistless eloquence of woe:

" Alas! my noble boy! that thou shouldst die!
    Thou, who were made so beautifully fair!
That death should settle in thy glorious eye,
    And leave his stillness in this clustering hair!
How could he mark thee for the silent tomb,
    My proud boy, Absalom!

" Cold is thy brow, my son! and I am chill
    As to my bosom I have tried to press thee!
How was I wont to feel my pulses thrill,
    Like a rich harp-string, yearning to caress thee,
And hear thy sweet 'My father!' from these dumb
    And cold lips, Absalom!

" But death is on thee. I shall hear the gush
    Of music, and the voices of the young;
And life will pass me in the mantling blush,
    And the dark tresses to the soft winds flung,—
But thou no more, with thy sweet voice, shalt come
    To meet me, Absalom!

" And, oh! when I am stricken, and my heart,
    Like a bruised reed, is waiting to be broken,
How will its love for thee, as I depart,
    Yearn for thine ear to drink its last deep token!
It were so sweet, amid death's gathering gloom,
    To see thee, Absalom!

" And now, farewell! 'Tis hard to give thee up,
    With death so like a gentle slumber on thee;
And thy dark sin!—Oh! I could drink the cup,
    If from this woe its bitterness had won thee.
May God have called thee, like a wanderer, home,
    My lost boy, Absalom!"

He covered up his face, and bowed himself
A moment on his child; then, giving him
A look of melting tenderness, he clasped
His hands convulsively, as if in prayer;
And, as if strength were given him of God,
He rose up calmly, and composed the pall
Firmly and decently, and left him there,
As if his rest had been a breathing sleep.

MISS ALBINA McLUSH

I HAVE a passion for fat women. If there is
    anything I hate in life, it is what dainty people
call a *spirituelle*. Motion—rapid motion—a smart,
quick, squirrel-like step, a pert, voluble tone—in
short, a lively girl—is my exquisite horror! I would
as lief have a *diable petit* dancing his infernal horn-
pipe on my cerebellum as to be in the room with
one. I have tried before now to school myself into
liking these parched peas of humanity. I have
followed them with my eyes, and attended to their
rattle till I was as crazy as a fly in a drum. I
have danced with them, and romped with them in

the country, and periled the salvation of my "white tights" by sitting near them at supper. I swear off from this moment. I do. I won't—no—hang me if ever I show another small, lively, *spry* woman a civility.

Albina McLush is divine. She is like the description of the Persian beauty by Hafiz: "Her heart is full of passion and her eyes are full of sleep." She is the sister of Lurly McLush, my old college chum, who, as early as his sophomore year, was chosen president of the *Dolce far niente* Society—no member of which was ever known to be surprised at anything—(the college law of rising before breakfast excepted). Lurly introduced me to his sister one day, as he was lying upon a heap of turnips, leaning on his elbow with his head in his hand, in a green lane in the suburbs. He had driven over a stump, and been tossed out of his gig, and I came up just as he was wondering how in the world they got there! Albina sat quietly in the gig, and when I was presented, requested me, with a delicious drawl, to say nothing about the adventure —it would be so troublesome to relate it to everybody! I loved her from that moment. Miss McLush was tall, and her shape, of its kind, was perfect. It was not a *fleshy* one exactly, but she was large and full. Her skin was clear, fine-grained and transparent; her temples and forehead perfectly rounded and polished, and her lips and chin swelling into a ripe and tempting pout, like the cleft of a bursted apricot. And then her eyes—large, liquid and sleepy—they languished beneath their long black fringes as if they had no business with daylight— like two magnificent dreams, surprised in their jet embryos by some bird-nesting cherub. Oh! it was lovely to look into them!

She sat, usually, upon a *fauteuil*, with her large, full arm embedded in the cushion, sometimes for hours without stirring. I have seen the wind lift the masses of dark hair from her shoulders when it seemed like the coming to life of a marble Hebe— she had been motionless so long. She was a model for a goddess of sleep as she sat with her eyes half closed, lifting up their superb lids slowly as you spoke to her, and dropping them again with the deliberate motion of a cloud, when she had murmured out her syllable of assent. Her figure, in a sitting posture, presented a gentle declivity from the curve of her neck to the instep of the small round foot lying on its side upon the ottoman. I remember a fellow's bringing her a plate of fruit one evening. He was one of your lively men—a horrid monster, all right angles and activity. Having never been accustomed to hold her own plate, she had not well extricated her whole fingers from her handkerchief before he set it down in her lap. As it began to slide slowly toward her feet, her hand relapsed into the muslin folds, and she fixed her eye upon it with a kind of indolent surprise, drooping her lids gradually till, as the fruit scattered over the ottoman, they closed entirely, and a liquid jet line was alone visible through the heavy lashes. There was an imperial indifference in it worthy of Juno.

Miss McLush rarely walks. When she does, it is with the deliberate majesty of a Dido. Her small, plump feet melt to the ground like snow-flakes; and her figure sways to the indolent motion of her limbs with a glorious grace and yieldingness quite indescribable. She was idling slowly up the Mall one evening just at twilight, with a servant at a short distance behind her, who, to while away the time between his steps, was employing himself in throwing stones at the cows feeding upon the Common. A gentleman, with a natural admiration for her splendid person, addressed her. He might have done a more eccentric thing. Without troubling herself to look at him, she turned to her servant and requested him, with a yawn of desperate ennui, to knock that fellow down! John obeyed his orders; and, as his mistress resumed her lounge, picked up a new handful of pebbles, and tossing one at the nearest cow, loitered lazily after.

Such supreme indolence was irresistible. I gave in—I—who never before could summon energy to sigh—I—to whom a declaration was but a synonym for perspiration—I—who had only thought of love as a nervous complaint, and of women but to pray for a good deliverance—I—yes—I—knocked under. Albina McLush! Thou were too exquisitely lazy. Human sensibilities cannot hold out forever.

I found her one morning sipping her coffee at twelve, with her eyes wide open. She was just from the bath, and her complexion had a soft, dewy transparency, like the cheek of Venus rising from the sea. It was the hour, Lurly had told me, when she would be at the trouble of thinking. She put away with her dimpled forefinger, as I entered, a cluster of rich curls that had fallen over her face, and nodded to me like a water-lily swaying to the wind when its cup is full of rain.

"Lady Albina," said I, in my softest tone, "how are you?"

"Bettina," said she, addressing her maid in a voice as clouded and rich as the south wind on an Æolian, "how am I to-day?"

The conversation fell into short sentences. The dialogue became a monologue. I entered upon my declaration. With the assistance of Bettina, who supplied her mistress with cologne, I kept her attention alive through the incipient circumstances. Symptoms were soon told. I came to the avowal Her hand lay reposing on the arm of the sofa, half buried in a muslin *foulard*. I took it up and pressed the cool soft fingers to my lips—unforbidden. I rose and looked into her eyes-for confirmation. Delicious creature! she was asleep!

I never have had courage to renew the subject. Miss McLush seems to have forgotten it altogether. Upon reflection, too, I'm convinced she would not survive the excitement of the ceremony—unless, indeed, she should sleep between the responses and the prayer. I am still devoted, however, and if there should come a war or an earthquake, or if the millennium should commence, as is expected in 18—, or if anything happens that can keep her waking so long, I shall deliver a declaration, abbreviated for me by a scholar-friend of mine, which, he warrants, may be articulated in fifteen minutes—without fatigue.

WILLIAM WORDSWORTH

WILLIAM WORDSWORTH, born in Cumberland, Eng., 70; died 1850. Cambridge gave him his collegiate raining. He was the founder of what is known s the "Lake School of Poetry." He gave his life his art; but full appreciation of his merits came his later days. His earlier poems as they appeared ere severely punished by the critics. But to-day e is recognized as one of England's foremost oets. In 1843 he succeeded Southey as poet laure-te. Wordsworth's most ambitious poem is "The xcursion," which is little read. His best work ap-ears in his short poems, especially descriptive of ature or suffused with elements of human interest.

INTIMATIONS OF IMMORTALITY, FROM RECOLLECTIONS OF EARLY CHILDHOOD

I

THERE was a time when meadow, grove and stream,
The earth, and every common sight,
        To me did seem
    Apparelled in celestial light,
The glory and the freshness of a dream.
It is not now as it hath been of yore;—
        Turn wheresoe'er I may,
        By night or day,
The things which I have seen I now can see no more!

II

The rainbow comes and goes,
And lovely is the rose;
The moon doth with delight
Look round her when the heavens are bare;
Waters on a starry night
Are beautiful and fair;
The sunshine is a glorious birth;—
But yet I know, where'er I go,
That there hath passed away a glory from the earth

III

Now, while the birds thus sing a joyous song,
And while the young lambs bound
As to the tabor's sound,
To me alone there came a thought of grief;
A timely utterance gave that thought relief;
And I again am strong.
The cataracts blow their trumpets from the steep—
No more shall grief of mine the season wrong:
I hear the echoes through the mountains throng
The winds come to me from the fields of sleep;
And all the earth is gay.
Land and sea
Give themselves up to jollity;
And with the heart of May
Doth every beast keep holiday:—
Thou child of joy,
Shout round me, let me hear thy shouts, thou happy
shepherd-boy!

IV

Ye blessèd creatures, I have heard the call
Ye to each other make; I see
The heavens laugh with you in your jubilee;

My heart is at your festival,
　　My head hath its coronal,
The fulness of your bliss I feel—I feel it all.
　　Oh, evil day! if I were sullen,
　　While Earth herself is adorning,
　　　This sweet May morning;
　　And the children are culling,
　　　On every side,
　　In a thousand valleys far and wide,
　　Fresh flowers; while the sun shines warm,
And the babe leaps up on his mother's arm:—
　　I hear, I hear, with joy I hear!
　　—But there's a tree, of many one,
A single field which I have looked upon—
Both of them speak of something that is gone:
　　　The pansy at my feet
　　　Doth the same tale repeat:
Whither is fled the visionary gleam?
Where is it now, the glory and the dream?

V

Our birth is but a sleep and a forgetting:
The soul that rises with us, our life's star,
　　Hath had elsewhere its setting,
　　　And cometh from afar;
　　Not in entire forgetfulness,
　　And not in utter nakedness,
But trailing clouds of glory do we come
　　　From God, who is our home:
Heaven lies about us in our infancy!
Shades of the prison-house begin to close
　　　Upon the growing boy;
But he beholds the light, and whence it flows,
　　　He sees it in his joy;
The youth, who daily farther from the east
　Must travel, still is Nature's priest,

And by the vision splendid
Is on his way attended;
At length the man perceives it die away,
And fade into the light of common day.

VI

Earth fills her lap with pleasures of her own;
Yearnings she hath in her own natural kind,
And, even with something of a mother's mind,
And no unworthy aim,
The homely nurse doth all she can
To make her foster-child, her inmate man,
Forget the glories he hath known,
And that imperial palace whence he came.

VII

Behold the child among his new-born blisses,
A six-years' darling of a pigmy size!
See, where 'mid work of his own hand he lies,
Fretted by sallies of his mother's kisses,
With light upon him from his father's eyes!
See, at his feet, some little plan or chart,
Some fragment from his dream of human life,
Shaped by himself with newly-learnèd art;
A wedding or a festival,
A mourning or a funeral;
And this hath now his heart,
And unto this he frames his song:
Then will he fit his tongue
To dialogues of business, love, or strife;
But it will not be long
Ere this be thrown aside,
And with new joy and pride
The little actor cons another part;
Filling from time to time his "humorous stage
With all the persons, down to palsied age,

That Life brings with her in her equipage;
   As if his whole vocation
   Were endless imitation.

VIII

Thou, whose exterior semblance dost belie
   Thy soul's immensity;
Thou best philosopher, who yet dost keep
Thy heritage; thou eye among the blind,
That, deaf and silent, readest the eternal deep,
Haunted forever by the eternal mind,—
   Mighty Prophet! Seer blessed!
   On whom those truths do rest,
Which we are toiling all our lives to find;
In darkness lost, the darkness of the grave;
Thou, over whom thy immortality
Broods like the day, a master o'er a slave,
A presence which is not to be put by;
Thou little child, yet glorious in the might
Of heaven-born freedom, on thy being's height,
Why with such earnest pains dost thou provoke
The years to bring the inevitable yoke,
Thus blindly with thy blessedness at strife?
Full soon thy soul shall have her earthly freight,
And custom lie upon thee with a weight,
Heavy as frost, and deep almost as life!

IX

   O joy! that in our embers
   Is something that does live,
   That nature yet remembers
   What was so fugitive!
The thought of our past years in me doth breed
Perpetual benedictions: not indeed
For that which is most worthy to be blessed;
Delight and liberty, the simple creed

Of childhood, whether busy or at rest,
With new-fledged hope still fluttering in his breast,—
> Not for these I raise
> The song of thanks and praise;
> But for those obstinate questionings
> Of sense and outward things,
> Fallings from us, vanishings;
> Blank misgivings of a creature
Moving about in worlds not realized,
High instincts, before which our mortal nature
Did tremble, like a guilty thing surprised:
> But for those first affections,
> Those shadowy recollections,
> Which, be they what they may,
Are yet the fountain light of all our day,
Are yet a master light of all our seeing;
> Uphold us, cherish, and have power to make
Our noisy years seem moments in the being
Of the eternal silence: truths that wake

> To perish never;
Which neither listlessness, nor mad endeavor,
> Nor man, nor boy,
Nor all that is at enmity with joy,
Can utterly abolish or destroy!
> Hence, in a season of calm weather,
> Though inland far we be,
Our souls have sight of that immortal sea
> Which brought us hither;
> Can in a moment travel thither,
And see the children sport upon the shore,
And hear the mighty waters rolling evermore.

X

Then sing, ye birds—sing, sing a joyous song!
> And let the young lambs bound
> As to the tabor's sound!
We, in thought, will join your throng,

Ye that pipe and ye that play,
Ye that through your hearts to-day
Feel the gladness of the May!
What thought the radiance which was once so bright
Be now forever taken from my sight,—
Though nothing can bring back the hour
Of splendor in the grass, of glory in the flower;
We will grieve not, rather find
Strength in what remains behind;
In the primal sympathy,
Which, having been, must ever be
In the soothing thoughts that spring
Out of human suffering;
In the faith that looks through death,
In years that bring the philosophic mind.

XI

And oh, ye fountains, meadows, hills, and groves,
Forbode not any severing of our loves!
Yet in my heart of hearts I feel your might;
I only have relinquished one delight,
To live beneath your more habitual sway.
I love the brooks, which down their channels fret,
Even more than when I tripped lightly as they;
The innocent brightness of a new-born day
Is lovely yet;
The clouds that gather round the setting sun
Do take a sober coloring from an eye
That hath kept watch o'er man's mortality:
Another race hath been and other palms are won.
Thanks to the human heart by which we live;
Thanks to its tenderness, its joys, and fears,
To me the meanest flower that blows can give
Thoughts that do often lie too deep for tears.

THE SEVEN SISTERS

SEVEN daughters had Lord Archibald,
  All children of one mother:
I could not say in one short day
What love they bore each other.
A garland of seven lilies wrought!
Seven sisters that together dwell;
But he—bold knight as ever fought—
Their father—took of them no thought,
He loved the wars so well.
Sing, mournfully, oh! mournfully,
The solitude of Binnorie.

Fresh blows the wind, a western wind,
And from the shores of Erin,
Across the wave a rover brave
To Binnorie is steering:
Right onward to the Scottish strand
The gallant ship is borne;
The warriors leap upon the land,
And hark! the leader of the band
Hath blown his bugle horn.
Sing, mournfully, oh! mournfully,
The solitude of Binnorie.

Beside a grotto of their own,
With boughs above them closing,
The Seven are laid, and in the shade
They lie like fawns reposing.
But now, upstarting with affright
At noise of man and steed,
Away they fly to left, to right—
Of your fair household, Father Knight,
Methinks you take small heed!
Singing, mournfully, oh! mournfully,
The solitude of Binnorie.

Away the seven fair Campbells fly,
And, over hill and hollow,
With menace proud, and insult loud,
The Irish rovers follow.
Cried they, "Your father loves to roam:
Enough for him to find
The empty house when he comes home;
For us your yellow ringlets comb,
For us be fair and kind.
Sing, mournfully, oh! mournfully,
The solitude of Binnorie.

Some close behind, some side by side,
Like clouds in stormy weather,
They run, and cry, "Nay let us die,
And let us die together."
A lake was near, the shore was steep,
There never foot had been;
They ran, and with a desperate leap
Together plunged into the deep,
Nor ever more were seen.
Sing, mournfully, oh! mournfully,
The solitude of Binnorie.

The stream that flows out of the lake,
As through the glen it rambles,
Repeats a moan o'er moss and stone,
For those seven lovely Campbells.
Seven little islands, green and bare,
Have risen from out the deep:
The fishers say, those sisters fair
By fairies are all buried there,
And there together sleep.
Sing, mournfully, oh! mournfully,
The solitude of Binnorie.

LUCY

SHE dwelt among the untrodden ways
   Beside the springs of Dove,
A maid whom there were none to praise,
   And very few to love.

A violet by a mossy stone
   Half hidden from the eye—
Fair as a star, when only one
   Is shining in the sky!

She lived unknown, and few could know
   When Lucy ceased to be;
But she is in her grave, and, oh,
   The difference to me!

SHE WAS PHANTOM OF DELIGHT

SHE was a phantom of delight
   When first she gleamed upon my sight;
A lovely apparition, sent
To be a moment's ornament;
Her eyes as stars of twilight fair;
Like twilight's, too, her dusky hair;
But all things else about her drawn
From May-time and the cheerful dawn;
A dancing shape, in image gay,
To haunt, to startle, and way-lay.

I saw her upon nearer view
A spirit, yet a woman too!
Her household motions light and free,
And steps of virgin liberty;
A countenance in which did meet
Sweet records, promises as sweet;

A creature not too bright or good
For human nature's daily food;
For transient sorrows, simple wiles,
Praise, blame, love, kisses, tears, and smiles.

And now I see with eyes serene
The very pulse of the machine;
A being breathing thoughtful breath,
A traveler betwixt life and death;
The reason firm, the temperate will,
Endurance, foresight, strength, and skill—
A perfect woman, nobly planned,
To warn, to comfort, and command;
And yet a spirit still and bright
With something of an angel light.

TO A SKY-LARK

ETHEREAL minstrel! pilgrim of the sky!
    Dost thou despise the earth where cares abound?
Or, while the wings aspire, are heart and eye
Both with thy nest upon the dewy ground?
Thy nest which thou canst drop into at will,
Those quivering wings composed, that music still!

To the last point of vision, and beyond,
Mount, daring warbler! that love-prompted strain
('Twixt thee and thine a never-failing bond)
Thrills not the less the bosom of the plain:
Yet might'st thou seem, proud privilege! to sing
All independent of the leafy spring.

Leave to the nightingale her shady wood;
A privacy of glorious light is thine;
Whence thou dost pour upon the world a flood
Of harmony, with rapture more divine;
Type of the wise who soar, but never roam;
True to the kindred points of heaven and home!

THE SOLITARY REAPER

BEHOLD her, single in the field,
  Yon solitary Highland Lass!
Reaping and singing by herself;
Stop here, or gently pass!
Alone she cuts, and binds the grain,
And sings a melancholy strain;
O listen! for the Vale profound
Is overflowing with the sound.

No Nightingale did ever chant
More welcome notes to weary bands
Of travelers in some shady haunt,
Among Arabian sands:
A voice so thrilling ne'er was heard
In spring-time from the Cuckoo-bird,
Breaking the silence of the seas
Among the farthest Hebrides.

Will no one tell me what she sings?
Perhaps the plaintive numbers flow
For old, unhappy, far-off things,
And battles long ago:
Or is it some more humble lay,
Familiar matter of to-day?
Some natural sorrow, loss, or pain,
That has been, and may be again!

Whate'er the theme, the Maiden sang
As if her song could have no ending;
I saw her singing at her work,
And o'er the sickle bending;—
I listened—motionless and still;
And when I mounted up the hill,
The music in my heart I bore,
Long after it was heard no more.

THE RAINBOW

MY heart leaps up when I behold
    A Rainbow in the sky:
So was it when my life began;
So is it now I am a Man;
So be it when I shall grow old,
      Or let me die!
The Child is Father of the Man;
And I could wish my days to be
Bound each to each by natural piety.

ÉMILE ZOLA

ÉMILE ZOLA, French novelist and dramatist, was born in Paris in 1840; died in 1902. He was educated at the Lycée, St. Louis, and entered a publishing house. He had always a strong desire to become famous as an author and wrote at odd hours, the "Contes à Ninon," which was published in 1864. From that time to his death he wrote almost constantly. He was a man of strong political views, and made during his career many bitter enemies. These, to him, only added to the excitement of existence. He was an intense realist, and found many of his plots and characters in subjects avoided by the majority of writers.

AFTER THE FIGHT

(From "The Attack on the Mill." By permission of Brentanos, publishers. Translated by E. P. Robins)

IT was three o'clock. The heavens were piled high with great black clouds, the tail-end of a storm that had been raging somewhere in the vicinity. Beneath the coppery sky and ragged scud the valley of Rocreuse, so bright and smiling in the sunlight, became a grim chasm, full of sinister shadows. The Prussian officer had done nothing with Dominique beyond placing him in confinement, giving no indication of his ultimate purpose in regard to him. Françoise, since noon, had been suffering unendurable agony; notwithstanding her father's entreaties she would not leave the courtyard. She was waiting for the French troops to appear, but the hours slipped by, night was approaching, and she suffered all the more since it

316

appeared as if the time thus gained would have no effect on the final result.

About three o'clock, however, the Prussians began to make their preparations for departure. The officer had gone to Dominique's room and remained closeted with him for some minutes, as he had done the day before. Françoise knew that the young man's life was hanging in the balance; she clasped her hands and put up fervent prayers. Beside her sat Father Merlier, rigid and silent, declining, like the true peasant he was, to attempt any interference with accomplished facts.

"Oh! my God! my God!" Françoise exclaimed, "they are going to kill him!"

The miller drew her to him and took her on his lap as if she had been a little child. At this juncture the officer came from the room, followed by two men conducting Dominique between them.

"Never, never!" the latter exclaimed. "I am ready to die."

"You had better think the matter over," the officer replied. "I shall have no trouble in finding some one else to render us the service which you refuse. I am generous with you; I offer you your life. It is simply a matter of guiding us across the forest to Montredon; there must be paths."

Dominique made no answer.

"Then you persist in your obstinacy?"

"Shoot me, and have done with the matter," he replied.

Françoise, in the distance, entreated her lover with clasped hands; she was forgetful of all considerations save one, she would have had him commit a treason. But Father Merlier seized her hands that the Prussians might not see the wild gestures of a woman whose mind was disordered by her distress.

"He is right," he murmured, "it is best for him to die."

The firing-party was in readiness. The officer still had hopes of bringing Dominique over, and was waiting to see him exhibit some signs of weakness. Deep silence prevailed. Heavy peals of thunder were heard in the distance, the fields and woods lay lifeless beneath the sweltering heat. And it was in the midst of this oppressive silence that suddenly the cry arose:

"The French! the French!"

It was a fact; they were coming. The line of red trousers could be seen advancing along the Sauval road, at the edge of the forest. In the mill the confusion was extreme; the Prussian soldiers ran to and fro, giving vent to guttural cries. Not a shot had been fired as yet.

"The French the French!" cried Françoise, clapping her hands for joy. She was like a woman possessed. She had escaped from her father's embrace and was laughing boisterously, her arms raised high in air. They had come at last, then, and had come in time, since Dominique was still there, alive!

A crash of musketry that rang in her ears like a thunder-clap caused her to suddenly turn her head. The officer had muttered. "We will finish this business first," and with his own hands pushing Dominique up against the wall of a shed, had given the command to the squad to fire. When Françoise turned Dominique was lying on the ground, pierced by a dozen bullets.

She did not shed a tear, she stood there like one suddenly rendered senseless. Her eyes were fixed and staring, and she went and seated herself beneath the shed, a few steps from the lifeless body. She looked at it wistfully; now and then she would make a movement with her hand in an aimless, childish way. The Prussians had seized Father Merlier as a hostage.

It was a pretty fight. The officer, perceiving that he could not retreat without being cut to pieces, rapidly made the best disposition possible of his men; it was as well to sell their lives dearly. The Prussians were now the defenders of the mill and the French were the attacking party. The musketry fire began with unparalleled fury; for half an hour there was no lull in the storm. Then a deep report was heard and a ball carried away a large branch of the old elm. The French had artillery; a battery, in position just beyond the ditch where Dominique had concealed himself, commanded the main street of Rocreuse. The conflict could not last long after that.

Ah! the poor old mill! The cannon-balls raked it from wall to wall. Half the roof was carried away; two of the walls fell in. But it was on the side toward the Morelle that the damage was greatest. The ivy, torn from the tottering walls, hung in tatters, débris of every description floated away upon the bosom of the stream, and through a great breach Françoise's chamber was visible with its little bed, the snow-white curtains of which were carefully drawn. Two balls struck the old wheel 'n quick succession and it gave one parting groan; buckets were carried away down stream, the ... ie was crushed into a shapeless mass. It was the soul of the stout old mill, parting from the body.

Then the French came forward to carry the place by storm. There was a mad hand-to-hand conflict with the bayonet. Under the dull sky the pretty valley became a huge slaughter-pen; the broad meadows looked on affrightedly, with their great isolated trees and their rows of poplars, dotting them with shade, while to right and left the

forest was like the walls of a tilting-ground in-
closing the combatants, and in nature's universal
panic the gentle murmur of the springs and water-
courses sounded like sobs and wails.

Françoise had not stirred from the shed, where she
remained hanging over Dominique's body. Father
Merlier had met his death from a stray bullet.
Then the French captain, the Prussians being ex-
terminated and the mill on fire, entered the courtyard at the head of his men. It was the first success
that he had gained since the breaking out of the
war, so, all afire with enthusiasm, drawing himself
up to the full height of his lofty stature, he laughed
pleasantly, as a handsome cavalier like him might
laugh, and perceiving poor idiotic Françoise where
she crouched between the corpses of her father and
her husband, among the smoking ruins of the mill,
he saluted her gallantly with his sword and shouted:

"Victory! victory!"